MW00636431

ENLIVEN
ENCOUNTERING GOL
through
HIS WORD

Romans

CHAPTERS 1-8

A PATH TO TRANSFORMATION

DISCOVERY GUIDE

FRENCH L. ARRINGTON, PH.D.

ISBN: 978-1-940682-40-2

TABLE OF CONTENTS

ROMANS CHAPTERS 1-8: REVIEW

SUPPLEMENTAL RESOURCE

ABOUT THE AUTHOR

INTRODUCTORY SESSION

INTRODUCTION TO INDUCTIVE STUDY OF ROMANS

INTRODUCTION

To Inductive Study of Romans

Key Verse

"And do not be conformed to this world, but be transformed by the renewing of your mind, that you may prove what is that good and acceptable and perfect will of God" (Romans 12:2).

Why Study Romans?

In Romans, Paul tells us to be transformed by the renewing of our minds (12:2). Our minds are renewed as we think about and mediate on the things of God. In another one of Paul's letters, his letter to the Philippian Christians, he instructs us to fill our minds with things that will inspire us to worship and serve God, and to be of service to others: *"whatever things are true, whatever things are noble, whatever things are just, whatever things are pure, whatever things are lovely, whatever things are of good report, if there is any virtue and if there is anything praiseworthy—meditate on these things."* (Phil. 4:8).

Many Christians are anxious and fearful, but the study of God's Word is a primary means of setting us free and giving us peace of mind. Jesus made it clear that the truth will set us free: *"If you abide in My word, you are My disciples indeed. And you shall know the truth, and the truth shall make you free"* (John 8:31-32). As you begin to think about inductive Bible study, consider the following questions:

☐ Do you have an interest in Bible study?

☐ Are you open to the message of the Scriptures?

☐ Have you laid the Bible aside because you did not think you could understand what God is saying to you and the significance of it for your life?

☐ Are you acquainted with a few passages in the Bible, but have a desire to know more about the Word of God?

☐ Are you unwilling or unable to discuss the teachings of Scripture because you are uncertain what you believe or do not feel you know the Bible well enough?

☐ Do you desire to know the great story of salvation better?

If your answer to any of these questions is yes, or if you have other reasons for studying the Bible, then this study of Romans is for you. In studying Romans, we can learn the content of the Christian faith like nowhere else in the Bible. Indeed Romans is God's story of salvation. This letter is sensible and draws powerful conclusions. The whole letter has pastoral and practical applications for the

Christian life, the church, and the world. In short, it shows a keen understanding of all our lives, plumbing the depth of the human heart and human existence.

Your Inductive Bible Study

The Four Steps. During your inductive Bible study of Romans, in order for you to receive maximum benefit in each lesson, you will begin by reading some introductory remarks to the passage of Scripture that you will be studying. You will then participate in four basic steps:

1—**DISCOVER**   (*observation*)

2—**DISCERN**   (*interpretation*)

3—**DEVOTE**   (*reflection & prayer*)

4—**DISCIPLE**   (*application*)

Pauses for Prayer. As you move through your study, you will be invited to *Pause for Prayer* and to become present with God during your study time. Bible study best takes place in an atmosphere of prayer, in conversation with God. The Holy Spirit has inspired the Word of God. What has been given by the Spirit is to be interpreted by the aid of the Spirit. Prayer opens our hearts to the Holy Spirit and allows Him to guide us in the learning process. Communication with and receptiveness to the Spirit bring forth truth from God's Word that stimulates discipleship and spiritual growth.

As you *Pause for Prayer* during your study time, there are various ways that you might choose to pray. In addition to inviting the Holy Spirit's presence into your time of study, you might thank God for His truths and blessings that you are receiving through His Word, or ask Him to move in a specific way in your life or in the world. During these moments of prayer, it can be helpful to focus on a particular passage from God's Word in a reflective, prayerful way. In this *Discovery Guide*, during your *Pause for Prayer*, you will be given an opportunity to reflect on and pray about passages from Romans.

STEP 1-DISCOVER

Observation: **Observe & Uncover the Facts** • **Using** *Helping Questions*

Asking: "What do I see in this passage?"

Each week following your reading of the introductory remarks in your *Discovery Guide* about the passage, the first step you will take in your own inductive Bible study of Romans will be to read and focus on the content of a portion of Scripture. This initial reading is best done carefully and prayerfully.

Using *Helping Questions.* To help you begin to **DISCOVER** (*uncover* and *observe*) the wonderful truths of God's Word, you will be asked to formulate questions that will help you notice and see the facts and truths in that particular passage of Scripture. In each lesson, you will be given the opportunity to create *Helping Questions* (asking Who? What? When? Where? Why? How?) in order to help you explore the biblical text.

As you begin to ask *Helping Questions*, be open to the Holy Spirit and what the writer is saying. You might want to make notes about any meanings that begin to emerge, so that you can explore them further when it is time to interpret and **DISCERN** the meaning of the text.

Each week during this **DISCOVER** point of your study, in addition to reading the biblical text and introductory remarks for the lesson and creating *Helping Questions*, you may also want to quickly review "LESSON ONE-Overview of Romans" to see where Paul is heading in his discussion.

STEP 2-DISCERN

Interpretation: **Interpret & Understand the Meaning** • **Using** *Helping Tools*

Asking: "What is the meaning of this passage?"

The Holy Spirit is our great teacher. He works together with us to illuminate our understanding, as we are steadfast in our study of God's Word. You remember Paul's words in 2 Timothy 2:15: "*Study to show yourself approved by God, a workman who need not be ashamed, rightly dividing the word of truth*" (MEV). Worthwhile Bible study involves real study and requires diligence on our part. There are great treasures to be *discovered* and *discerned* by studying the Word. In each lesson, we will ask for the Holy Spirit's help as we begin to *discern* (*interpret*) the truths in a particular passage of God's Word.

Using *Helping Tools.* During this second **DISCERN** step of your study, you will have the opportunity to mark important words and phrases. Using colored pencils or highlighters, you will get to be creative and have fun underlining, circling, highlighting, or marking in some way phrases and verses. These markings that you apply will be your *Helping Tools* that will assist you in discerning the meaning of the passage.

As you mark the text, you will begin to notice some key terms and concepts, and will also see some patterns and repetitions emerging in Paul's discussion. Use whatever markings work best for you. This step is meant to be a fun one that helps you personally. Some examples of *Helping Tools* that you might create are:

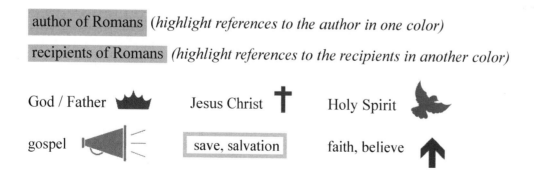

author of Romans (*highlight references to the author in one color*)

recipients of Romans (*highlight references to the recipients in another color*)

God / Father 👑   Jesus Christ ✝   Holy Spirit 🕊

gospel 📢   save, salvation   faith, believe ⬆

Discerning what the Bible says. Once you have marked the text with your *Helping Tools*, you will begin to explore the meaning of the passage by looking for the meaning in the Bible itself. In inductive Bible study, the meaning of a passage is always to be explored in the Bible first, in light of the passage's context within the book of the Bible of which it is a part.

As you look over the passage that you have marked with *Helping Tools*, carefully think about the words and reflect on them. Should you struggle with the *interpretation (the meaning)*, you may want to refer to some Bible study aids such as a commentary, Bible dictionary, word study, or other theological work. The recommended commentary for this study is a basic one on Romans, *The Greatest Letter Ever Written*, by French L. Arrington, published by Pathway Press. If you use a study Bible, the recommended choice is the *Fire Bible*. It is a Pentecostal study Bible with emphasis on the Christian life, baptism in the Spirit, and gifts of the Spirit. It is available in *King James Version*, *New International Version*, and *English Standard Version*. (For a list of additional print and online resources, see "Helpful Supplies & Resources" at the end of this INTRODUCTORY SESSION.)

Using Various Bible Versions. The Protestant principle is that each person is to be encouraged to read the Bible in his or her own language. The scriptural quotations of this publication, unless otherwise indicated, will be from the *New King James Version* (NKJV). Along with using the NKJV, comparison of different translations can be very helpful for gaining a fuller understanding of the passage you are studying. BibleGateway.com and BibleStudyTools.com are good online resources for Bible version comparison.

STEP 3-DEVOTE

Reflection & Prayer: **Reflect, Pray & Be Transformed •**

Through Conversation with God & Journaling

Asking: "God, what do You want to say to me through your Word?"

We study God's Word to be changed and to be strengthened, not merely to accumulate information. That is why you are studying to understand a passage of Scripture—so that you can experience the transforming power of truth.

Once you have completed the **DISCOVER** and **DISCERN** steps, it is important to take some time to reflect and pray about what you have learned and experienced during your time of study. God wants to speak to you and bless you. This **DEVOTE** (*reflection and prayer*) step of inductive Bible study is a wonderful opportunity for you to experience God in a fresh, new way. During this time, you may *devote* (dedicate) yourself to God and His call by reflecting on His Word, receiving instruction from Him, and allowing His Spirit to change, bless, and equip you.

A good way to begin this special devotion time with God is to sit quietly in His presence for a few moments, inviting Him to quiet your mind and to help you focus on Him. In each lesson, you will be given an opportunity to prepare your heart through a *Pause for Prayer*, in which you will be invited to reflect on a verse of Scripture.

Following your reflection on God's Word, you will then encounter in your *Discovery Guide* a few reflection questions for that particular lesson that will help you open your heart to God and ask Him how He wants to use this passage of Scripture to transform you.

In addition to considering these reflection questions, you may also want to look through any notes that you have made in your journal or *Discovery Guide*, to help you identify how God wants to move in your heart and life.

Some possible questions that you might want to ask God during this **DEVOTE** step of your inductive Bible study are:

- ☐ God, who are You calling me to be—How do You want to change and transform me?

- ☐ Do You want to clarify any misperceptions that I might have had in the past?

- ☐ Are You calling me to repentance and change in any areas of my life?

- ☐ How do You want me to grow, especially in faith and trust in You?

- ☐ In what ways are You calling me to a deeper level of commitment to You and Your Word?

- ☐ What would You have me do in light of what I have learned?

- ☐ Are You calling me to some new aspect of service or ministry?

Remember, this is time for a very personal conversation with God during which He wants to bless you. As you receive knowledge, healing, inspiration, direction, or inclinations of calling, be sure to note those in your notebook or journal. This way you will have them to return to later for remembering, further exploration, prayer, or action.

STEP 4-DISCIPLE

Application: **Apply & Live God's Word • Through Commitment & Action**

Asking: *(1) "What is the meaning for today—in my life and in the world?"*

   (2) "How can and will I act on what I have learned?"

The next natural step following your **DEVOTE** time with God is for you to begin to live what you have learned—to be a *disciple*. This will involve your taking what you have experienced with God during this study and putting it into action—in your own life, within your relationship with others, and out in the larger world.

In this **DISCIPLE** step of inductive Bible study, you will have an opportunity to ask God through His Holy Spirit to direct you and give you wisdom regarding what actions He is calling you to take. God promises that He will help each of us in this process. Through the power of His Spirit, we can grow and make changes in our lives, and develop new habits and ways of being and doing things. We can also learn how to share our personal experiences of God's saving love with others in ways that are unique to us, using the gifts and talents God has given us. We can learn to be disciples and make disciples (Matt. 28:19).

As you think about how the passage of Scripture you are studying applies to the church and the world today, ask God how you might move forward in living out the truths of His Word. Consider if you want to make any commitments or make any plans to do so. You might note any thoughts, inspirations, creative ideas, commitments, plans, or questions in your notebook or journal, so that you have them for future reference for action, prayer, or sharing with others.

Instructions for Using Your *Discovery Guide*

As part of each lesson, you will begin by reading the *Key Verse* and an Introduction to the passage of Scripture you will be studying. You will then be invited to *Pause for Prayer*, following which you will read the actual text of the passage of Scripture. Once you have completed your reading, you will begin to move through your inductive Bible study steps: **DISCOVER**, **DISCERN**, **DEVOTE**, and **DISCIPLE**.

Along the way, while moving through your *Discovery Guide*, you will be invited to interact with the text in various ways. You may be asked to complete a sentence, list your ideas, answer questions, rewrite a scriptural thought in your own words, compare the Scripture with other passages, identify a core focus and other major themes (subjects) of the passage, or to do other similar activities. Please take each exercise seriously. Think about what you are being asked to do. After you have written your answer, read it carefully and prayerfully. You may want to revise it and rewrite it, as you gain more insight. What you write is for your own benefit; it will not be judged or read by anyone else. In group sessions, you will be asked to share only what you are comfortable sharing.

Inductive Bible study allows you to teach yourself. If you are a part of a class or a group that is doing this study, you will likely have the opportunity to share from time to time some of your thoughts, feelings, or insights with others in your group. As a member of a class or study group, it is very important that you do the exercises of the assigned lesson before you meet each time, so that you are prepared to gain from and contribute to the group's time together.

As you go through your *Discovery Guide*, you may come across some words or phrases that are unfamiliar to you. If so, for help you may wish to turn to the appendix "God's Plan of Salvation" in the back of this *Discovery Guide*, as well as to the glossary in French Arrington's commentary on Romans, *The Greatest Letter Ever Written*, pages 435-467. Here and there in your *Discovery Guide* you will find references to Arrington's commentary. This commentary is recommended to help you understand doctrinal ideas and teachings. Also, the maps on pages 424-428 of that commentary will help you locate the places mentioned in Romans. You may also find that a Bible dictionary is helpful.

Before you begin to work your way through Lesson One, we want to thank you for joining in this study. Our hope is that your time spent in Romans will be a satisfying and rewarding experience and an exciting adventure. Above all, we pray that you will be transformed and strengthened by the study of God's Word. Do not let anyone or anything discourage you from the study of the inspired Word of God. It takes time and discipline. That is what discipleship is all about. May God bless you as you study His Word!

Helpful Supplies & Resources

ESSENTIAL:

- ☐ *Romans: A Path to Transformation (Chapters 1–8). Discovery Guide.* French L. Arrington. Church of God Adult Discipleship, 2015.

- ☐ A study Bible—such as *Fire Bible* (NIV 1984, KJV, or ESV), Hendrickson Publishers. (Former titles: *Full Life Study Bible* and *Life in the Spirit Study Bible*).

- ☐ Colored pens or pencils, highlighters

- ☐ Notebook or journal

RECOMMENDED:

- ☐ Commentary—*The Greatest Letter Ever Written: A Study of the Book of Romans.* French L. Arrington. Pathway Press, 2012.

- ☐ How to do inductive Bible study—*Enliven Encountering God Through His Word* Bible study. William A. Simmons. Church of God Adult Discipleship, 2014, 2016.

ONLINE:

☐ *BibleGateway.com* www.biblegateway.com
Offers various Bible versions and study tools.

☐ *BibleStudyTools.com* www.biblestudytools.com

Offers various Bible versions and study tools, including a helpful word study resource Strong's Exhaustive Concordance (linked from KJV and NASB to Hebrew and Greek lexicons).

☐ Additional online tools, such as:

Biblia.com, BlueLetterBible.org, and StudyLight.org.

OPTIONAL:

Your local public or church library may have the following types of resources in their reference or circulating collections:

☐ Bible handbook—such as: *Halley's Bible Handbook*. Henry H. Halley. Zondervan, 2014.

☐ Bible commentary—one-volume or a multi-volume set, such as *Zondervan Illustrated Bible Backgrounds Commentary*. Clinton E. Arnold. Zondervan, 2002.

☐ Bible dictionary, encyclopedia, or concordance, such as:

Evangelical Dictionary of Biblical Theology. Walter A. Elwell. Baker Books, 2001. 1996 edition: http://www.biblestudytools.com/dictionaries/.

Strong's Exhaustive Concordance—

The New Strong's Expanded Exhaustive Concordance of the Bible. James Strong. Thomas Nelson, 2010. Online: www.biblestudytools.com, search in KJV or NASB, and select "Interlinear" to view the concordance linked to Hebrew and Greek lexicons.

Vine's Complete Expository Dictionary of Old and New Testament Words. W. E. Vine, Merrill F. Unger, William White, Jr. Thomas Nelson, 1996.

A Closing Prayer of Blessing

"Grace and peace be yours in abundance through the knowledge of God and of Jesus our Lord.

His divine power has given us everything we need for a godly life through our knowledge of him who called us by his own glory and goodness." (2 Peter 1:2-3, NIV)

LESSON ONE

Romans

CHAPTERS 1-16

OVERVIEW

LESSON ONE

ROMANS: CHAPTERS 1—16

OVERVIEW

Key Verse

For I am not ashamed of the gospel of Christ, for it is the power of God to salvation for everyone who believes, for the Jew first and also for the Greek. For in it the righteousness of God is revealed from faith to faith; as it is written, "The just shall live by faith" (Romans 1:16-17).

Welcome

Welcome to your inductive study of Romans. The book of Romans is a letter from Paul to the Roman church. It is considered by Christians to be the greatest letter ever written because of its remarkable influence on the church throughout history. You are about to begin an exploration of one of the most exciting letters in the New Testament and in the world through the ages. This *Discovery Guide* focuses on Romans chapters 1–8. The sequel study to this one will cover chapters 9–16.

Background of Romans

The Importance of Romans

Throughout the history of the Christian Church, the epistle to the Romans has had a strong influence. At a very early time, the importance of Romans was indicated by the church through its placement in the New Testament. Though Paul had written five letters before Romans (1st and 2nd Thessalonians, Galatians, and 1st and 2nd Corinthians), Romans stands first among them. The early church placed Romans before the other epistles because of its content rather than its age.

Scholars throughout history have been heavily impacted by the content of Romans. Irenaeus, one of the great thinkers of the early church and the bishop of Lyons in Gaul, reflected the strong influence of Romans in his teachings. This letter from Paul to the Romans brought the famous church father, Augustine, to a life–changing experience when he read Romans 13:13-14.

Romans provided impetus for the Protestant Reformation in the sixteenth century and was the scriptural basis for Luther's protest against the spiritual condition of the church at that time. Two centuries later, an evangelical movement was begun by John and Charles Wesley. On one occasion John Wesley was present for the reading of Martin Luther's commentary on Romans. The words of Paul, interpreted by Luther, brought the heartfelt, transforming power of the gospel to bear on Wesley's life. From that time on, his ministry and theology were profoundly influenced by Romans.

The Holy Spirit has continued to use Romans as a major source to bring about revivals and renewal movements. Indeed, Romans is an important key for understanding the rest of the Bible—both the Old and New Testaments. The best summary to Christian doctrine in the sixty-six books of the Bible, it has had a remarkable influence for twenty centuries. It will continue to have a vast influence until Jesus comes because its content so magnifies the glories of the Lord's gospel.

The Author—The Apostle Paul

Paul's Background. It is believed that Paul wrote the epistle to the Romans. Biblical scholars have never seriously questioned that he was the author of this letter. Both Paul's letters and the Book of Acts provide us with several facts about him:

☐ Paul was born in the Greek city of Tarsus in Asia Minor to Jewish parents who belonged to the strict political-religious party of the Pharisees.

☐ He studied in Jerusalem under the great rabbi Gamaliel, probably preparing to become a religious teacher.

☐ He became an ardent opponent of the Christian church.

☐ While Paul was engaging in persecution of Christians, on the road to Damascus, he had a life-changing experience with the risen Christ. As a result of his conversion and call to ministry, Paul became the most vigorous of Christian missionaries and led the way in the opening of Christian fellowship to non-Jews.

Paul's Ministry. Assisted by others, Paul preached the gospel in the Greek and Roman world during three extensive journeys:

First Journey—Paul's first journey lasted about three years, taking him to the island of Cyprus and Asia Minor.

Second Journey—His second also lasted about three years. It took him across Asia Minor, where he revisited the churches that he had planted during his first journey. He then traveled on into Europe, where he established churches in the cities of Philippi, Thessalonica, and Corinth.

Third Journey—During Paul's third journey, he covered much the same route as the second. This journey included a stay of about three years in Ephesus. From Ephesus, he traveled west through Macedonia to Greece (Corinth) where he wrote his marvelous letter "To all who are in Rome, beloved of God…" (Rom. 1:7). Paul probably wrote Romans in A.D. 58, just before he departed for the holy city of Jerusalem carrying with him an offering for Christians who were suffering in poverty.

During his third journey, Paul was in the process of completing his ministry in the eastern Mediterranean world and was thinking about expanding his ministry to the west. He was planning to visit Rome and then take the gospel into Spain (Rom. 15:19-28), but when he arrived in the city of Jerusalem with funds for the impoverished Christians, the apostle was accused of religious heresy and political sedition, and was arrested. After he was held in custody for two years, Paul was sent to Rome as a prisoner. According to tradition, Paul was put to death in A.D. 67 by the hand of the Roman emperor Nero in the city of Rome.

The Location—Rome

The City of Rome. Rome was the center and capital of the Roman Empire, which controlled the world reaching from Egypt to Britain and from Palestine to Spain. With its great military power, Rome dominated the entire civilized world. We do not know how Christianity reached Rome nor anything about how the church was established in that city. Neither Paul nor Peter had visited Rome before Paul wrote his letter to the Christians there.

The church in Rome. The Roman church was strong, and their commitment to Christianity had been reported throughout the Roman Empire (Rom. 1:8). It is believed by many that the church was established by Roman pilgrims who had been among those who were present in Jerusalem on the Day of Pentecost. Mostly likely, those Roman pilgrims were in the crowd that heard Peter preach that day (Acts 2:10, 14). After receiving the gospel, they would have returned to Rome, and then possibly organized the church. Another possibility is that some Christians from the Pauline churches had moved to Rome and then established the church there.

Paul's letter to the Romans shows that the Christian community consisted of both Jewish believers (1:13; chapters 9–11) and Gentiles believers (2:9-10; 11:13). Most likely, the majority were Gentiles (1:5, 13-15), especially since of the 26 people mentioned in chapter 16, only 15 percent of them were Jewish. Though in the minority, the Jews had considerable influence in the church.

The Purpose of Romans

Guided by the Holy Spirit, Paul had a number of reasons for writing this magnificent letter to the Roman believers. His letter indicates that his reasons for writing were due to his own situation, as well as that of the Roman Christians. He had a growing desire to visit Rome and to preach the gospel there (1:15).

Paul wanted:

☐ **To introduce himself and his message.**

Though Paul had never been to Rome, as an apostle to the Gentiles, he had universal binding authority over the church, including the Roman church (Rom. 11:13; Gal. 2:8). In the introduction of his letter, Paul gives a lengthy and logical overview of his message. The tone of his introduction may hint that false rumors may have been circulating about his message and ministry. He had been criticized in the Jewish world for preaching a law-free gospel. So in some measure, Paul probably wanted to deny the rumors that he was a divisive and dangerous person who was preaching a heretical message. The entire letter to the Romans clarifies his message.

☐ **To offer pastoral encouragement to the church.**

Though Paul had never been to Rome, he and the Roman Christians were not complete strangers. He tells them that their faith had been proclaimed throughout the world (1:8) and that they are, "full of goodness, filled with all knowledge, able to admonish one another" (15:14). No doubt, Paul felt some pastoral responsibility for the Roman believers (1:11; 15:14-16). In his heart, Paul had warm feelings and concerns for them.

☐ To appeal for financial support.

One of the reasons for Paul's writing this letter is expressed in the words, "to be helped on my way there by you" (15:24). The word "there" refers to Spain and "to be helped" (*sent*) was almost a technical missionary term, meaning not only "to send forth" with goodwill and prayer, but also with food and money. Paul desired that the Roman church assume some financial responsibility for his mission into Spain and hoped that the letter would convince them that his Spanish ministry was worthy of their support.

☐ To prepare for a new home base.

Paul had made Antioch in Syria his home base during his ministry in the East. Now he was anticipating ministering in the West and would need another home base for the next phase of his ministry. Rome would be ideal, since it was the capital of the Roman Empire and the hub of the Mediterranean world where many people came and went. Furthermore, the strong church in Rome could support his vision for evangelism in the West.

☐ **To request prayer.**

Planning to depart from Corinth on his way to Jerusalem with the funds for the needy Christians, Paul was uncertain what kind of reception he might receive. His first concern was about hostile unbelievers in Judea, because they had tried to kill him on a previous visit (Acts 9:29). His second concern was whether or not the Jewish Christians would accept the financial gift from the Gentile churches. Paul's request was that the Roman Christians pray for these two concerns (15:30-31).

☐ **To proclaim the gospel.**

The Apostle desired to be an evangelist while in Rome. In the opening chapter of Romans, we read, "So, as much as is in me, I am ready to preach the gospel to you who are in Rome also" (1:15).

Paul wanted the Roman Christians to know what to expect while he was among them, But contrary to his anticipation, he did not arrive in Rome as an evangelist, but as a prisoner in chains.

A Summary of Romans

Paul, in writing to the church in Rome, was writing to a church that he had neither established nor with which he had previous communication. In his letters to other churches, Paul had dealt with specific questions and problems. With the exception of Colossians, those letters were addressed to churches that Paul had established himself. Romans, however, is a more general letter dealing with more general theological issues.

In his letter to the Romans, Paul sets forth the nature of the gospel and confronts the Roman church (and us) with the truths of God. He exposes our inclination to try to save ourselves, and emphasizes that our salvation is wholly due to the grace of God. Paul demolishes any human claims of self-sufficiency, and lays bare the fact that we all must one day face our inexcusable guilt before God. The only hope for each of us is repentance and faith through the atoning death of Jesus Christ.

Major themes and concerns. Briefly stated, Paul's major themes in Romans are: our need for salvation, God's grace and our faith, the scope of salvation, and Christian life and service. Other major concerns of his are: the gospel of Jesus Christ, the righteousness of God, the law, and the two ages.

Particular issues in the Roman church. Even though Romans is a more general letter, Paul does show that he is acquainted with the Roman church and speaks to a few particular problems and situations among the Romans believers (11:13-25; 13:1-7; 14:2-10).

The Six Parts of Romans

The content of Romans can be divided into six major parts for our convenience of studying:

Part 1—Introduction (1:1-17). The first part of Romans is Paul's introduction of himself and his message. In his opening words, Paul identifies himself and presents his credentials. He was writing to a church that did not know him well. Aware that there may have been some misunderstandings regarding his message, he defines his message as "the gospel [Good News] of Christ" (1:16) and mentions some of the topics that he will cover in his letter: his apostolic authority, the fulfillment of the Old Testament in the gospel, the gospel of salvation centered in Jesus Christ, obedience involved in faith, and his mission to the Gentiles. Using his favorite title for Christians, Paul speaks of the Christians in Rome as saints and pronounces a blessing on them (1:7).

Part 2—Salvation (1:18 – 5:21). The second part of Romans deals with the need for and the nature of salvation. The fundamental concern is, "How can a person be forgiven of personal sin and brought into right relationship with God?" Paul explains that it is through the gospel of Jesus Christ that a person is saved—brought into right relationship with Him and into a state of eternal life. This condition of life is brought about by God's saving power received in faith, a faith that involves repentance and trusting in God for salvation.

Both the Jews and Gentiles had failed to keep the Mosaic law, and in so doing, stood under the wrath (holy displeasure) and judgment of God (1:18–3:20). However, Paul proceeds to show that God's righteousness (justifying, saving power) has been revealed in Jesus Christ apart from the law (3:21–5:21). The righteousness of God is placed on the account of all who believe in Jesus Christ as their Savior (3:22). "All have sinned" clearly shows that sin is universal and has touched every person's life (3:23). The sin problem can be solved by Christ who bestows the gift of eternal life. Any person who accepts God's gracious gift offered in Christ will be saved, but no amount of obedience to God's law can result in any claim on God or the right to eternal life.

Part 3—Sanctification (chapters 6–8). The third major part of Romans addresses the need for sanctification. Paul asks that after being saved, "Shall we continue in sin?" His answer is emphatically, "Certainly not!" He insists that salvation, which is received through faith (rather than by observing the law) should increase our efforts to live a holy life (6:1-2). Sin has no place at all in the Christian's life. Scripture identifies this type of life as sanctification (holy living) (John 17:15-17). A right relationship requires a decisive break with sin.

Paul develops the doctrine of sanctification by explaining the concept of the believer's freedom from the power of sin and how to become mature and holy in character (chapter 6), freedom from the condemnation of the law (chapter 7), and freedom from death at resurrection (chapter 8). Sanctification is continuous and ongoing throughout life, and is experienced by living and serving God. (For a brief explanation of sanctification, see also appendix: "God's Plan of Salvation" in this *Discovery Guide*.)

Part 4—God's Chosen People (chapters 9–11). The fourth part of Romans addresses a perplexing problem: Why had God's chosen people as a whole not accepted Jesus and followed Him as their Savior? (chapters 9–11). At the beginning of his letter, Paul mentions that the gospel was offered first to the Jews (1:16). However, the Gentiles had been more receptive to God's plan of salvation than God's own people. Chapters 9–11 of Romans are best understood as Paul's need to explain why the Gentiles outnumbered the Jews in the church at that time. By the time Paul wrote

Romans, the concern seems to have been threefold: (1) Why had Christianity become predominantly a Gentile religion? (2) Had God been fair to Israel and kept His promises to them? (3) Had Paul turned against his own people and tried to destroy the law of Israel? Paul addresses these important issues in this part of his letter.

Part 5—Christian Living (12:1–15:31). The fifth part of Romans focuses on Christian conduct, which is a vital dimension of sanctification. Paul has already discussed sanctification (chapters 6–8), but at this point he deals with its practical application. Beginning with chapter 12, he turns his attention to the everyday life of believers, indicating how they should relate to other people both in the church and in the world. In the first 11 chapters, Paul has mainly discussed doctrine, but in 12:1 the "therefore" marks Paul's shift of thought to the discussion of everyday living. What the Bible teaches is not only to be understood, but is to be applied and experienced in daily life. Paul affirms this concept by joining instructions for ethics in everyday living with his theological and doctrinal teachings.

A few details that Paul addresses in this section of Romans are:

☐ *Romans 12*—rules that are to govern the common life in the church, with an emphasis on humility in exercising spiritual gifts;

☐ *Romans 13*—proper relations between the state and its citizens; and

☐ *Romans 14 and 15*—the strife that had developed between the vegetarians and meat-eaters, and between those who had religious scruples about holy days and those who did not.

Part 6—Closing (15:14 – 16:27). The sixth part of Romans is the closing of Paul's letter. Paul started his letter with personal remarks about himself and his work. Now he returns to personal matters and his ministry among the Gentiles. He expresses his interest in the Roman church and his future plans of going to Rome, and then on into Spain. We do not know if he ever went to Spain. If he did, it was after he spent about four years in confinement in Caesarea and Rome. Chapter 16 of Romans includes a long list of people to whom Paul sends his greetings.

Your Exploration of the Text

Now you will begin your own personal exploration of Romans. As you begin your time of study, first take a few moments to *Pause for Prayer* and to invite God into your time with His Word.

Pause for Prayer

"All Scripture is given by inspiration of God, and is profitable for doctrine, for reproof, for correction, for instruction in righteousness, that the man of God may be complete, thoroughly equipped for every good work" (2 Timothy 3:16-17).

God, You inspired the Apostle Paul to write the book of Romans.

As I begin my study of Your inspired Word, open my mind and heart to You and Your truths, so that I may learn more about Your plan of salvation, follow in Your way, and be complete.

Romans Overview

As you start your study of this wonderful book of the Bible, consider and answer the questions below. In answering the questions, you may use the introductory discussion, as well as consult other resources such as a study Bible, a Bible commentary (such as *The Greatest Letter Ever Written*, by French Arrington), or a Bible handbook.

1. Briefly describe the city of Rome, Paul's relationship with the city, and who established the church there.

   _____

   _____

   _____

   _____

   _____

   _____

2. There are a variety of reasons for people to study the Bible. What are your reasons for studying Paul's great letter to the Roman Christians?

   _____

   _____

_____

_____

_____

_____

3. Perhaps you have done Bible studies before, or you have preached or heard several sermons. At this time, what is your understanding of Paul's message to the Romans?

_____

_____

_____

_____

_____

_____

_____

_____

_____

4. To get a good sense of the entire text of Romans, read through it in one sitting.

Following your reading, answer the question: What is your understanding of the major themes and concerns of these chapters? List them in brief form in the table below. (For assistance see "A Summary of Romans" above in LESSON ONE, and Arrington's comments on pages 21-23; 42-46 of his commentary *The Greatest Letter Ever Written*.)

Major Themes of Romans	
Scripture Passages	Your Description
Our need: 1:18–3:31 (*3:9, 20, 23)	
God's part and our part: 4:13-25 (*4:16) 3:22; 5:1-2; 15-21; 10:9-13	
See also the appendix: "God's Plan of Salvation" in this *Discovery Guide*. People: 1:16; 3:21-26; 10:12-13 Creation: 8:19-21	
Instructions for living: 12:1–15:13 (*12:1-2, 4-8, 9-10; *13:8, 11-14; *14:13; *15:2, 7)	

Some Major Concerns of Paul	
Scripture Passages	Your Description
1:1-6, 9, 15-17; 15:16, 19; 16:25	
1:17; 3:21-26	
3:20; 5:20; 7:1-25	
5:12-21	

5. In light of your reading through chapters 1–16 of Romans, answer two questions:

    (1) Who can be saved? (2) On what condition? Explain on the basis of the biblical text.

    _____

    _____

    _____

    _____

    _____

    _____

6. Summarize Paul's three missionary journeys. Indicate the location where he wrote Romans, his

    circumstances, and the date he wrote it. (For maps, see Arrington's commentary, pages 424-428.)

Missionary Journey	Date	Places	Description
1st			
2nd			

3rd			
Writing of Romans:			

7. Paul had several reasons for writing his letter to the Romans. What seems to you to be the most important reason and why?

_____

_____

_____

_____

_____

8. Why has Romans been such an important letter in the history of the Church and remains to be so today?

_____

_____

_____

_____

_____

_____

_____

9. Summarize the message of Paul's letter to the Romans.

_____

_____

_____

_____

_____

_____

Inductive Bible Study Method Review

The method of *Inductive Bible Study* may be new to you. To be sure that you understand it, read the section entitled "Introduction to Inductive Study of Romans" in this *Discovery Guide*.

1. Identify the four steps of inductive Bible study, and briefly explain each step.

_____

_____

_____

_____

_____

_____

_____

2. Explain why prayer is an essential component of the Bible study process.

_____

_____

_____

_____

_____

_____

A Closing Prayer

Key Verse:

"For I am not ashamed of the gospel of Christ, for it is the power of God to salvation for everyone who believes, for the Jew first and also for the Greek. For in it the righteousness of God is revealed from faith to faith; as it is written, 'The just shall live by faith'" (Romans 1:16-17).

Lord Jesus Christ, thank You for your saving love.

In the weeks ahead during this study, I pray that You will help me to develop a deeper appreciation and understanding of Your life-changing gospel—and to discover how I might share Your Good News with others.

LESSON TWO

Romans

CHAPTERS 1:1-17

OPENING OF PAUL'S LETTER

LESSON TWO

ROMANS: 1:1–17

OPENING OF PAUL'S LETTER

Key Verse

"I am a debtor both to Greeks and to barbarians, both to wise and to unwise. So, as much as is in me, I am ready to preach the gospel to you who are in Rome also" (Romans 1:14-15).

Introduction

We come now to lesson two, moving from our quick overview of the entire book of Romans to taking a closer look at the first passage. Ancient letters normally opened with the name of the author, the name of the recipient, and a short greeting (examples: Acts 15:23; 23:26). Paul follows this pattern. In his opening remarks, in addition to his greeting, Paul also mentions briefly topics he will be addressing in his letter. He then later expands and elaborates on those topics. As is typical in Paul's letters (with the exception of Galatians), he includes a word of thanksgiving for his readers.

Paul's authority. In his opening in verse 1, Paul presents his credentials, indicating his authority for writing. The Christians in Rome may have known that Paul's authority as an apostle was being challenged due to the fact that he had not been one of the twelve apostles chosen by Jesus during Jesus' earthly ministry. In his greeting, Paul immediately affirms that he has been chosen by God and sent on a mission of service to Christ and preaching the Good News. His desire is to visit the Roman Christians so that he might impart to them some spiritual gift. No explanation of spiritual gifts is offered here in the opening, but Romans 12:6-8 and 1 Corinthians 12 give us a good idea of the types of gifts to which Paul refers.

Paul's relationship with the recipients of his letter. The gospel that Paul has been set apart to preach had been promised many years earlier by the Old Testament prophets. The prophets' message was now fulfilled through Christ's life, death, and resurrection. Because of what God did through Christ, the Roman Christians were a blessed people. In verse 7, Paul uses his favorite way of referring to the members of the Christian community—the word "saints." The saints were all set apart for the use and service of God. The Apostle greets the Roman Christians with a double blessing: grace and peace, a combination included in Paul's greetings in all of his letters (1:7). This blessing is an indication that when Paul thought about the Roman believers, he had reasons to be thankful for them and to pray for them.

Paul's travel plans. We do not know how long the Apostle Paul had been planning to go to Rome. Perhaps he had been hindered because of his duties in Asia Minor and Greece. Anyway, he wanted to go to the great city of Rome, so that he could have some fruit among the church there, as well as impart to them some spiritual gift. At least three years passed before Paul arrived in Rome—as a prisoner (Acts 28:16).

Paul's intent. Set apart as an apostle of Jesus Christ, Paul felt compelled to preach the gospel to as many people as possible, regardless of their station in life. Romans 1:16-17 reflects Paul's desire, as well as the theme of his entire letter: *"For I am not ashamed of the gospel of Christ, for it is the power of God to salvation for everyone who believes, for the Jew first and also for the Greek. For in it the righteousness of God is revealed from faith to faith; as it is written, 'The just shall live by faith'."* These two verses contain key words that will occur throughout Paul's letter to the Roman Christians. They also serve as a summary of the gospel, communicating the way that God provides salvation for all people who believe in Jesus Christ.

Your Exploration of the Text

Pause for Prayer

"For I long to see you, that I may impart to you some spiritual gift, so that you may be established—that is, that I may be encouraged together with you by the mutual faith both of you and me" (Romans 1:11-12).

God, You give wisdom to those who ask—both through Your Word and through those You send our way.

I ask You for wisdom as I study Your Word. Help me to understand Your truths and to grow my faith. Help me to be an encouragement to those who are on this journey with me, and to be open to receiving wisdom and encouragement from them.

THE TEXT

Romans 1:1-17

[1] Paul, a bondservant of Jesus Christ, called to be an apostle, separated to the gospel of God [2] which He promised before through His prophets in the Holy Scriptures, [3] concerning His Son Jesus Christ our Lord, who was born of the seed of David according to the flesh, [4] and declared to be the Son of God with power according to the Spirit of holiness, by the resurrection from the dead. [5] Through Him we have received grace and apostleship for obedience to the faith among all nations for His name, [6] among whom you also are the called of Jesus Christ;

[7] To all who are in Rome, beloved of God, called to be saints:

Grace to you and peace from God our Father and the Lord Jesus Christ.

[8] First, I thank my God through Jesus Christ for you all, that your faith is spoken of throughout the whole world. [9] For God is my witness, whom I serve with my spirit in the gospel of His Son, that without ceasing I make mention of you always in my prayers, [10] making request if, by some means, now at last I may find a way in the will of God to come to you. [11] For I long to see you, that I may impart to you some spiritual gift, so that you may be established— [12] that is, that I may be encouraged together with you by the mutual faith both of you and me.

[13] Now I do not want you to be unaware, brethren, that I often planned to come to you (but was

hindered until now), that I might have some fruit among you also, just as among the other Gentiles. [14]

I am a debtor both to Greeks and to barbarians, both to wise and to unwise. [15] So, as much as is in me,

I am ready to preach the gospel to you who are in Rome also.

[16] For I am not ashamed of the gospel of Christ, for it is the power of God to salvation for everyone

who believes, for the Jew first and also for the Greek. [17] For in it the righteousness of God is revealed

from faith to faith; as it is written, "The just shall live by faith."

DISCOVER

Your personal study of Romans now begins by your observing the text and seeking to discover the facts that are revealed in this opening section of Paul's letter. To help you in your observation and discovery of Romans 1:1-17, you will begin by creating some *Helping Questions*.

Observing the Text

Helping Questions. In this first step of your study, read carefully Romans 1:1-17 and the Introduction for this passage. As you are moving through your reading of the biblical text, create some *Helping Questions* (WHO – WHAT – WHERE – WHEN – WHY – HOW) to help you discover the text.

To get you started, here are just a few examples of some *Helping Questions* that could be asked about this passage:

(1:1, 8-16)   Who is the author of this book of the Bible, and what do we know about him?

(1:7)   In what form is this book written, and for whom is it written?

(1:7)   What type of blessing does Paul give the recipients of his writing?

As you create your own *Helping Questions*, answer the ones you can. It's okay if you create questions for which you don't know the answers. You will have opportunity to explore those later during your own study time and during your group's time together. Later you can come back and fill in the answers. Record your questions and any answers that you know in the space below.

My Helping Questions and Answers:

_____

_____

_____

_____

_____

_____

Observations. Now that you have moved through the text discovering and observing it, briefly summarize what you have discovered. (Remember in the **DISCOVER** step you are only noting the obvious, the facts. You will explore the deeper meaning in the next step—**DISCERN**.)

My Findings:

_____

_____

_____

_____

DISCERN

You are now well on your way to uncovering the truths in this passage, and are ready for the next step! In this **DISCERN** step, you will take the observations that you made in your **DISCOVER** step and explore them more deeply to determine the meaning of what Paul wrote.

Marking the Text

Helping Tools. To help you discern the meaning, go through the passage again underlining, highlighting, or marking with symbols—key words, ideas, phrases, concepts, or anything that jumps out at you. Feel free to mark the text in a way that will be most meaningful to you. Your marks will be your *Helping Tools* that will help you discern the meaning of the text.

Tips for marking the text:

☐ **Creating** *Helping Tools* **for references to God.** Create a symbol for each member of the Holy Trinity (Godhead), then place the appropriate symbol above the name when Paul mentions it. Also consider highlighting references to God in yellow, so that they stand out among all the other items you will be marking. This yellow highlighting will also be helpful in cases where God (including members of the Godhead) is mentioned later in the same sentence or paragraph, and you do not want to fill the page with repeated symbols. (For sample symbols, see "Examples of *Helping Tools*.")

Key Concepts:

To help you get started, the next page contains some concepts and terms to explore, along with some examples of *Helping Tools* that one might create for this passage of Scripture. As you create your own *Helping Tools*, plan to use them throughout your study, so that you can easily follow Paul's discussion from passage to passage.

*PLEASE NOTE: In the following list, concepts and their descriptions are in regular font, and any sample terms from the actual biblical text are in italics.

- God–names for God and words describing members of the Holy Trinity (*Jesus Christ, God, He, Son, Lord, Father, Spirit, spiritual*)
- God's Word–*Holy Scriptures, is written*
- Gospel
- People–author (*Paul, I*), recipients of his letter (*you, saints, brethren*), *David*, particular groups of people (*Jews, Gentiles, Greeks, Barbarians*)
- Serve–*bondservant, serve, obedience*
- Faith–*faith, believe*
- Death / Resurrection
- Called
- Unity–*together, mutual*
- Debtor (bound by duty, under obligation)
- Miscellaneous:
  - Geographical locations–*nations, Rome, world*
  - Numbers or amounts–*all, whole*
  - ***TIP:** Mark with a hash mark (#).
  - Indications of time–*ready*
  - Comparisons, contrasts, repetitions, or progressions and sequences

- Prayer
- Righteousness of God:
  God's holiness and purity–*holiness, righteousness* (1:4, 17)
- Righteousness of People:
  Those in a right, holy standing with God through faith and holiness of heart and life–*just, live by faith* (1:17)
- Blessings–*grace, peace*
- Salvation
- Give / Receive–*gift, impart / receive*
- Speak–*spoken, witness, teach/preach concept*
- Fruit
- EXAMPLES:
  - REPITITION–*gospel*
  - PROGRESSION–*spiritual gift→you may be established* (1:11)
  - ONE OF MORE FOCUS VERSES:
    - KEY VERSE: 1:14-15
    - OTHER–1:1, 16-17
- Any other concepts you want to mark

Examples of *Helping Tools*:

author of Romans *(highlight references to the author in one color)*

recipients of Romans *(highlight references to the recipients in another color)*

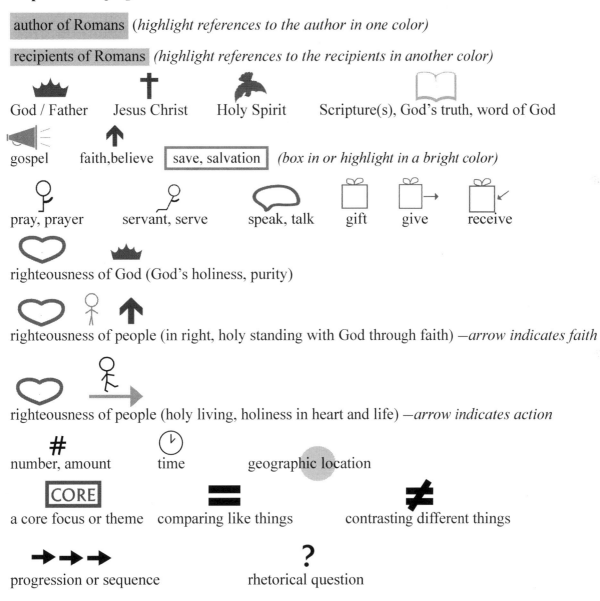

God / Father   Jesus Christ   Holy Spirit   Scripture(s), God's truth, word of God

gospel   faith, believe   save, salvation   *(box in or highlight in a bright color)*

pray, prayer   servant, serve   speak, talk   gift   give   receive

righteousness of God (God's holiness, purity)

righteousness of people (in right, holy standing with God through faith) —*arrow indicates faith*

righteousness of people (holy living, holiness in heart and life) —*arrow indicates action*

number, amount   time   geographic location

CORE   a core focus or theme   comparing like things   contrasting different things

progression or sequence   rhetorical question

Interpreting the Meaning

Following are questions to help you gain more understanding about the text. Please answer them in the space provided.

1. List here just a few main points that Paul makes in this passage that are of particular interest to you, and indicate how you feel about the opening of the letter.

_____

_____

_____

_____

2. Tell how Paul identifies himself to the Roman Christians, noting especially the significance of, "separated to the gospel of God" (v. 1). Why was it important for Paul (and all ministers of the gospel) to have a profound sense of being set apart for a specific purpose?

_____

_____

_____

_____

3. What are the personal characteristics that distinguished Paul as an able minister of the gospel?

_____

_____

_____

4. State the significance of the contrast: Jesus was born of the family of David, Israel's greatest king, but the Holy Spirit declared Him to be the Son of God.

    _____

    _____

    _____

    _____

5. See Romans 8:11 for the role that the Holy Spirit had in the resurrection of Christ, and explain what Paul means by "the Spirit of holiness" (1:4).

    _____

    _____

    _____

    _____

6. The phrase "obedience to the faith" (v. 5) can be translated "believing obedience," meaning obedience that flows out from saving faith. On the basis of Romans chapters 1–8, what do you think it means?

    _____

    _____

    _____

    _____

    _____

_____

_____

7. As is common in Paul's letters, he pronounces the blessing of grace and peace upon his readers (v. 7). Why do you think Paul uses this combination to bless them, and who is the source of this blessing?

_____

_____

_____

_____

_____

8. Paul was a man of prayer. Though he had never been to Rome, he had not failed to pray for the Roman believers and to be thankful for them. Why had he been thankful for that church, and what are some of the ways we can follow Paul's example?

_____

_____

_____

_____

_____

_____

9. One reason Paul gives for going to Rome was to impart to the Roman Christians some spiritual gift (v. 11). He wanted to be helpful, but did he really have the capacity to bestow on Christians spiritual gifts? Likely, he used a shorthand way of saying it, but meant that he would lay hands on them and pray for the Holy Spirit to impart to them gifts of the Spirit. In 1 Corinthians 12:7, Paul teaches that it is the Holy Spirit who gives spiritual gifts, not the minister of the gospel who gives them.

    In view of Romans 12:6-8 and 1 Corinthians 12, what were some of the spiritual gifts that Paul may have had in mind, and why would he have wanted the Christians in Rome to receive some of these gifts?

    _____

    _____

    _____

    _____

    _____

10. Paul was obligated to both the Greeks and the barbarians (1:14). By the time of Paul, the word "Greeks" had lost its national and racial/ethnic meaning and was a designation for language and culture. Philip II of Macedon and his son Alexander the Great, through their military exploits, had spread the Greek language and culture over the Roman Empire. Greek was a beautiful, flexible, harmonious language. All other people groups in the Roman Empire were called barbarians

because they did not speak Greek. In the same verse, "both to wise and to unwise" refers to "both the educated and uneducated."

The Apostle Paul placed himself under the obligation of every person in the Roman Empire. What was his obligation?

_____

_____

_____

_____

_____

_____

Under what obligation and to whom has your faith in Christ placed you? In what sense is every believer a debtor?

_____

_____

_____

_____

_____

_____

_____

_____

_____

_____

11. Romans 1:16-17 is a summary of the gospel of Jesus Christ, and the remainder of Romans is a commentary on these verses. These two verses include a number of key words that occur throughout the letter. Since the meaning of each of the words is crucial to our understanding of the message of Romans, provide a definition of each of the terms listed below. (Should at this point you need some assistance, do not hesitate to consult the glossary in Arrington's commentary, the appendix "God's Plan of Salvation" in this *Discovery Guide*, or a Bible dictionary.)

Gospel	
Power	
Salvation	

Faith	
Righteousness	
Live (*noun* Life)	

12. Paul stated that he was not ashamed of the gospel of Christ (Rom. 1:16), even though to preach Christ crucified was to the Jews a stumbling block and to the Greeks foolishness (1 Cor. 1:23). There was nothing for Paul to be ashamed about, for the gospel is God's power to bring people to salvation. His statement in 1:16 can be read as a positive declaration: "I am proud of the Good News" (NCV) or "I have complete confidence in the gospel" (GNT).

What specific reasons do you have for being proud of the gospel?

_____

_____

_____

_____

13. The phrase "from faith to faith" is a difficult one (1:17). You may want to consult other translations. After your exploration, indicate your own personal understanding of the meaning.

_____

_____

_____

_____

14. Romans 1:16-17 is packed with truth. Write in your own words these verses and make it clear according to verse 16 who can be saved, and according to verse 17 on what condition.

_____

_____

_____

_____

15. The quotation in verse 17 is from Habakkuk 2:4, a Jewish prophet who wrote in about 605 B.C. The original meaning of this text was that those who remained faithful to God's instructions would survive the coming siege of Jerusalem. This quotation is Paul's first citation of the Old Testament in Romans, but as we continue our study, you will note that he frequently quotes the Old Testament. Three questions:

Why does Paul look back to the Old Testament?

_____

_____

_____

_____

_____

What does he mean by his use of Habakkuk 2:4? Is its meaning the same in Romans 1:17 as in the Old Testament, or is it different? Explain.

_____

_____

_____

_____

What do you think of the Old Testament?

_____

_____

_____

_____

16. The word "gospel" means "good news." Some limit the gospel to justification by faith, but why should we think of the salvation provided by Jesus as including the past, present, and future? (For help, see the appendix "God's Plan of Salvation" in this *Discovery Guide*.)

_____

_____

_____

_____

_____

Pulling It All Together

Core focus and major themes. Look over Romans 1:1-17, once again noticing the *Helping Tools* that you have applied to the text. Are there any terms or concepts repeated? These will help point to major themes (major points that Paul is making). Consider marking or noting themes in the text in a way that is helpful to you—maybe by making notations in the margins alongside the biblical text.

In the following table, list at least one core focus for this passage, other major themes you have identified, and what this passage reveals about God's nature.

Core Focus:	

Major Themes:	
Nature of God:	

Summary. Now that you have used *Helping Tools* and answered the questions above to explore and discern the meaning of the text, briefly summarize your own interpretation—what you think Paul is saying in the text.

My Interpretation

_____

_____

_____

_____

_____

_____

_____

_____

_____

DEVOTE

Following your exploration of the meaning of the passage, take a few moments to reflect on what you have discerned, and talk to God about it.

☐ Invite God to use His Word to change you in any way He desires and to direct you in how you might apply His Word to your life.

☐ Consider writing in a journal or notebook your prayers, inspirations, or any decisions that you make during this time with God.

Pause for Prayer

"Draw near to God and He will draw near to you..." (James 4:8).

God, I come to You now. As You have promised, be with me, speak to my heart during this time we have together.

For Reflection & Prayer

Here are some questions you might consider discussing with God during this time of prayer. JUST A REMINDER: As you pray, remember to record in your prayer journal any thoughts that come to mind, which you want to remember.

☐ What has the gospel, the Good News of Jesus Christ and salvation, meant to your life?

☐ Are there any areas of your life in which you want to invite God's gifts of grace and peace?

☐ Consider asking God to teach and direct you in how you might extend His Good News and grace and peace to others.

☐   Are there any additional concerns you wish to pray about?

DISCIPLE

Following your time of devotion, the next natural step is to apply to your life the truths of this passage and what God has spoken to your heart—to begin to live God's truths. As you determine what God is calling you to do, consider writing any decisions or commitments in your journal or notebook.

Living and Sharing Your Faith

"Through Him [Jesus Christ] we have received grace and apostleship for obedience to the faith among all nations for His name" (Romans 1:5).

There is so much bad news in today's world. Many people need and want to hear the Good News, but some Christians are either ashamed of the gospel or are afraid that they may offend someone if they share it. The Holy Spirit has promised to give us boldness in sharing this powerful message of the gospel.

☐   Where might be some places where you have an opportunity to share the Good News of the gospel?

☐   Is there a unique way that you can share the gospel—using your own unique personality, abilities, spiritual gifts, or life circumstances?

☐ What kind of help do you need from God to fully use your unique spiritual gifts and abilities to share His Good News with others? Ask Him for this help. He wants to guide you and partner with you as you share His love with others.

☐ Are there any commitments that you feel God is leading you to make at this time?

☐ Is there any specific action you would like to take in response to what you have learned during your time in God's Word this week? Ask the Holy Spirit to help you, and take one small step in the direction that you feel Him leading you.

A Closing Prayer

Key Verse:

"I am a debtor both to Greeks and to barbarians, both to wise and to unwise. So, as much as is in me, I am ready to preach the gospel to you who are in Rome also" (Romans 1:14-15).

Lord, You offer each of us Your Good News of saving grace, no matter what our background or station in life.

Help me to be like Paul and to be courageous and willing to reach out with Your Good News to anyone You send my way.

ENLIVEN
ENCOUNTERING GOD
through
HIS WORD

LESSON THREE

Romans

CHAPTERS 1:18-2:29

THE WORLD'S NEED OF SALVATION

LESSON THREE

ROMANS: 1:18—2:29

THE WORLD'S NEED OF SALVATION

Key Verse

"For the wrath of God is revealed from heaven against all ungodliness and unrighteousness of men, who suppress the truth in unrighteousness, because what may be known of God is manifest in them, for God has shown it to them." (Romans 1:18-19).

Introduction

Romans 1:18 begins the main portion of Paul's letter. In this section, he contends that all humankind is guilty before God and in need of salvation. Apart from God's grace, all people are in bondage to sin and can do nothing to save themselves, not even through efforts to be obedient to God's law. The only hope that humankind has is the saving mercy and grace of God revealed in the gospel.

Paul's discussion about our need for salvation really continues through 3:20. (We will explore the last part in LESSON FOUR.) In his discussion about people's need for God, Paul communicates that humankind has sinned against God the Creator, the source of life and light. People's lack of understanding of who God is and their disrespect have placed them in a state of darkness from which they need to be saved. To prove this, Paul first addresses the Gentiles (1:18-32) and then the Jews (2:1 – 3:20).

The Gentiles. Paul paints a dark picture of the Gentile world. Remember that Paul was in Corinth, a city known for vices, corruption, and immorality, when he wrote Romans. The people's ungodly living had aroused God's wrath, His holy displeasure, toward their sins. Therefore, Paul in his letter declares that God's wrath is revealed from heaven against those who hold down and suppress the truth by their immoral living (1:18).

Creation reveals that God is God, making known His eternal power and Godhead (1:20). God's revelation of himself through creation is adequate to hold everyone accountable for their seeking or not seeking God. In Paul's day, many did not take the manifestation of God's nature through his creation seriously. Paul indicates that people are not excused on the grounds of ignorance of God's laws. Even though they may not know particular laws, all people are held accountable for neglecting what they do know and what is plain to all through creation. In His displeasure, God gave the rebellious Gentiles up to their vile passions and allowed them to plunge deeper and deeper into degrading behaviors and sensual pleasures (1:24, 26, 28).

In chapter 2, Paul speaks of the wrath of God as being a present reality here and now, but he also speaks of God's future wrath on the Day of Judgment (2:5). On that day, God will examine people's actions. He will judge on the basis of grace those who seek and follow His ways, honoring and rewarding them for their good deeds. He will judge those who are rebellious and self-seeking on the basis of the law, expressing His holy displeasure and allowing them to reap the consequences of their evil deeds.

The Final Judgment lies in the future, but it was already beginning in that God was allowing His holy displeasure and opposition toward sin (wrath) to be experienced by the Gentiles. They began to reap the natural consequences of their choices and actions, which were outside and contrary to God and His true way of love (1:18). God's judgment rests on what each person has done (2:6), meaning that God does not favor either the Jewish person or the Gentile person. In spite of the grim picture in Romans 1:18-32, there were Gentiles who sought for glory, honor, and incorruption (2:7) and did good (2:7, 10). When Paul speaks about doing good, he does not mean that Jews or Gentiles can earn salvation. To the contrary, in Paul's discussion, doing good is the fruit of faith and hope in Jesus Christ, which will be examined on the Day of Judgment.

Moving on, Paul mentions the relationship of the Gentiles to the law (2:12-16). The Gentiles had not received the Mosaic law, but the Jews had. A basic difference between Jews and Gentiles was not simply a matter of race or ethnicity but also of revelation. We should not assume that the Gentiles had no law at all. They had a basic law (knowledge of good and evil) written in their hearts. Every person is created in the image of God. Since God has the ability to discern between right and wrong, so do humans. Without the law given at Sinai, a Gentile is still held responsible for personal acts of sin by the law written in the heart. According to Paul, the function of the conscience is to judge conduct by the law written in the heart. This being said, the conscience is not an infallible guide. The ideal is that the conscience of a believer will make accurate decisions because it is enlightened by the Holy Spirit. But the conscience of Christian can err if he or she does not live in complete obedience to the will of God.

The Jews. At this point in 2:17-29, Paul turns from discussing the Gentiles to discussing those Jews who were self-righteous in their beliefs. They had taken pride in their possession of the Mosaic law and had boasted about being God's people. They had broken God's law, even though they had thought of themselves as spiritual guides and teachers of the truth (2:19-20). Paul exposes their hypocrisy by noting that they had committed the sins of theft, adultery, and idolatry against which they had taught (2:21-23). He points out that their failure to keep the law has been notice by the Gentiles (2:24).

For the Jews, the possession of the law was a hallmark of distinction, and circumcision was a symbol of their identity as the covenant people of God (Rom. 2:25-29). Many Jews believed that circumcision provided them with the right to entry into heaven regardless of their character. According to Paul, circumcision has no real spiritual value apart from faith and obedience (2:25). Paul's argument is twofold: (1) As a sign of the covenant God made with Israel, circumcision was to motivate holy living. (2) Circumcision is beneficial if the whole law is kept. As is made clear later, the perfect observance of the law by human strength is impossible (3:20; 7:7-25). Paul proceeds to redefine the terms "Jews" and "circumcision" (2:28-29). Being a true Jew was not just a matter of having the visible mark of Jewish piety.

Your Exploration of the Text

Pause for Prayer

"For since the creation of the world His invisible attributes are clearly seen, being understood by the things that are made, even His eternal power and Godhead..." (Romans 1:20).

Father, You are Creator of everything. Through Your natural world and order, You have shown us who You are, and have loved and provided for us.

Thank You for always loving me and wanting what is best for me. As I study, please show me any areas that I may need to submit to You for forgiveness and healing.

THE TEXT

Romans 1:1-18 – 2:29

Chapter 1:18-32

[18] For the wrath of God is revealed from heaven against all ungodliness and unrighteousness of men,

who suppress the truth in unrighteousness, [19] because what may be known of God is manifest in them,

for God has shown it to them. [20] For since the creation of the world His invisible attributes are clearly

seen, being understood by the things that are made, even His eternal power and Godhead, so that they

are without excuse, [21] because, although they knew God, they did not glorify Him as God, nor were

thankful, but became futile in their thoughts, and their foolish hearts were darkened. [22] Professing to

be wise, they became fools, [23] and changed the glory of the incorruptible God into an image made like

corruptible man—and birds and four-footed animals and creeping things.

[24] Therefore God also gave them up to uncleanness, in the lusts of their hearts, to dishonor their

bodies among themselves, [25] who exchanged the truth of God for the lie, and worshiped and served

the creature rather than the Creator, who is blessed forever. Amen.

[26] For this reason God gave them up to vile passions. For even their women exchanged the natural use for what is against nature. [27] Likewise also the men, leaving the natural use of the woman, burned in their lust for one another, men with men committing what is shameful, and receiving in themselves the penalty of their error which was due.

[28] And even as they did not like to retain God in their knowledge, God gave them over to a debased mind, to do those things which are not fitting; [29] being filled with all unrighteousness, sexual immorality, wickedness, covetousness, maliciousness; full of envy, murder, strife, deceit, evil-mindedness; they are whisperers, [30] backbiters, haters of God, violent, proud, boasters, inventors of evil things, disobedient to parents, [31] undiscerning, untrustworthy, unloving, unforgiving, unmerciful; [32] who, knowing the righteous judgment of God, that those who practice such things are deserving of

death, not only do the same but also approve of those who practice them.

Chapter 2:1-29

[1] Therefore you are inexcusable, O man, whoever you are who judge, for in whatever you judge another you condemn yourself; for you who judge practice the same things. [2] But we know that the judgment of God is according to truth against those who practice such things. [3] And do you think this, O man, you who judge those practicing such things, and doing the same, that you will escape the judgment of God? [4] Or do you despise the riches of His goodness, forbearance, and longsuffering, not knowing that the goodness of God leads you to repentance? [5] But in accordance with your hardness and your impenitent heart you are treasuring up for yourself wrath in the day of wrath and revelation

of the righteous judgment of God, [6] who "will render to each one according to his deeds": [7] eternal life to those who by patient continuance in doing good seek for glory, honor, and immortality; [8] but to those who are self-seeking and do not obey the truth, but obey unrighteousness—indignation and wrath, [9] tribulation and anguish, on every soul of man who does evil, of the Jew first and also of the Greek; [10] but glory, honor, and peace to everyone who works what is good, to the Jew first and also to the Greek. [11] For there is no partiality with God.

[12] For as many as have sinned without law will also perish without law, and as many as have sinned in the law will be judged by the law [13] (for not the hearers of the law are just in the sight of God, but the doers of the law will be justified; [14] for when Gentiles, who do not have the law, by nature do the things in the law, these, although not having the law, are a law to themselves, [15] who show the work

of the law written in their hearts, their conscience also bearing witness, and between themselves their thoughts accusing or else excusing them) [16] in the day when God will judge the secrets of men by Jesus Christ, according to my gospel.

[17] Indeed you are called a Jew, and rest on the law, and make your boast in God, [18] and know His will, and approve the things that are excellent, being instructed out of the law, [19] and are confident that you yourself are a guide to the blind, a light to those who are in darkness, [20] an instructor of the foolish, a teacher of babes, having the form of knowledge and truth in the law. [21] You, therefore, who teach another, do you not teach yourself? You who preach that a man should not steal, do you steal? [22] You who say, "Do not commit adultery," do you commit adultery? You who abhor idols, do you rob

temples? [23] You who make your boast in the law, do you dishonor God through breaking the law? [24]

For "the name of God is blasphemed among the Gentiles because of you," as it is written.

[25] For circumcision is indeed profitable if you keep the law; but if you are a breaker of the law, your

circumcision has become uncircumcision. [26] Therefore, if an uncircumcised man keeps the righteous

requirements of the law, will not his uncircumcision be counted as circumcision? [27] And will not

the physically uncircumcised, if he fulfills the law, judge you who, even with your written code

and circumcision, are a transgressor of the law? [28] For he is not a Jew who is one outwardly, nor is

circumcision that which is outward in the flesh; [29] but he is a Jew who is one inwardly; and circumcision

is that of the heart, in the Spirit, not in the letter; whose praise is not from men but from God.

DISCOVER

You are now ready to begin your exploration of Romans 1:1-18 – 2:29, observing the text and discovering the facts.

Observing the Text

Helping Questions. Read carefully Romans 1:1-18 – 2:29. As you are moving through your reading of the biblical text, create some *Helping Questions* to help you discover the text. As you create your *Helping Questions*, answer the ones you can. Consider marking the ones to which you don't know the answer, so you can come back to them later either in your personal study or during group discussion. Record your questions and any answers in the space below.

My Helping Questions and Answers:

_____

_____

_____

_____

_____

_____

_____

Observations. Now that you have moved through the text discovering and observing it, briefly summarize what you have discovered. (Remember in the **DISCOVER** step you are only noting the obvious, the facts. You will explore the deeper meaning in the next step—**DISCERN**.)

My Findings:

_____

_____

_____

_____

_____

DISCERN

Now that you have observed the text and discovered some facts, it is time to take a closer look, to explore the meaning of what Paul is communicating in this section of his letter to the Romans.

Marking the Text

Helping Tools. To help you discern the meaning, go through the passage again underlining, highlighting, or marking with symbols—key words, ideas, phrases, concepts, or anything that jumps out at you.

Tips for marking the text:

- ☐ **Reusing symbols from last week.** As you study the biblical text, you will encounter some of the same terms that you marked last week in LESSON TWO. Be sure to use the same markings for repeated concepts.

- ☐ **Creating a master list of your** *Helping Tools.* Make a list of the *Helping Tools* that you have used, in order make it easier in future lessons for you to be consistent in the way that you mark the text.

- ☐ **How to mark negatives.** One way to mark negatives, is to create a HELPING TOOL symbol for a positive term, then negate it by drawing a line through it. (See below: "Examples of *Helping Tools.*")

- ☐ **Marking Paul's comments about Gentiles and Jews.** In 1:18-32, Paul talks about the Gentiles. In 2:1-29 (and 3:1-20 of LESSON FOUR), Paul talks about the Jews. Mark each of these sections using different colors and/or symbols. Using one color, you might mark the beginning of his discussion about the Gentiles with the letter "G," then use the letter "J" (in another color) to mark his discussion about the Jews. To show where each discussion ends, you might insert an asterisk in the appropriate color.

Key concepts:

Following are some concepts that you might consider marking. To help give you some ideas for creating and using *Helping Tools*, see "Example *Helping Tools*" that follows this list.

- Concepts mentioned in this passage for which you already created *Helping Tools* in LESSON TWO
- God (names and terms for members of the Holy Trinity)
- God's truth and self-revelation–*truth, the law*, creation/natural order. ***TIP:** Look for the verbs: *reveal, manifest*, and *show*
- People–humans (*men, women*) Gentiles–*do not have the law*, Jews–*in the law*. ***TIP:** For ideas for marking entire sections about the Gentiles and Jews, see above: "Tips for marking the text."
- Knowledge, understanding
- Righteousness of God:
  - God's holiness–*incorruptible (1:23)*
  - Rightness and holiness of God's judgments–*righteous judgment (1:32; 2:5)*
  - Rightness and holiness of God's law (holy in a moral sense, being right and from God)–*righteous requirements (2:26)*

- Ungodly–*ungodliness*
- Serve, worship–*glorify, worship, serve, obey*
- Sin-*sin, ungodliness, unrighteousness, dishonor, evil, lie*, idolatry (*creature, image, idols*)… ***TIP:** Consider underlining or boxing in all references to sin using the color BLACK, leaving space above the term, just in case you want to tag a particular type of sin with its own Helping Tool.
- Consequences of sin-*wrath of God, indignation/penalty, tribulation, anguish*
- Repentance
- Wise/Unwise concepts. ***TIP:** Create a symbol for the word "*wise*," then draw a line through it to indicate the concept of *being unwise*.
- *(2:13)*Witness–*bear witness, accusing* (legal terms)
- Judgment – *judge, judgment, condemn (*legal terms*)*
- Blessings–*riches, goodness, forbearance, longsuffering, eternal life…*
- Honor – *glory, blessed, honor, praise*
- The law – *law, written code*

- ■ Righteousness of people:
  - • In a right, holy standing with God through faith–*justified*
  - • Unrighteousness, unholiness in heart and life–*unrighteousness, uncleanness (1:18, 24, 29; 2:8).*
    TIP: Draw a HELPING TOOL for *righteousness,* then draw a line through it to indicate *"unrighteousness"* (See below: "Examples of *Helping Tools.*")
- ■ Religious observances and rituals–*circumcision*
- ■ Miscellaneous:
  - • Numbers or amounts–*all, as many*
  - • Indications of time–*since*
  - • Rhetorical questions–***TIP:** Mark with a question mark (?) at the beginning of the question.
  - • Comparisons, contrasts, repetitions, or progressions and sequences:

EXAMPLES:
- • COMPARISON–legal imagery: *judge, condemn, law...*
- • CONTRAST–*wise/fools; incorruptible God/corruptible man (1:22, 23*
- • REPETITION–*wrath, judge/judgment, honor/dishonor.*
- • SEQUENCE–*the Jew first → also of the Greek (2:9, 10)*
- • One or more focus verses:
  - ○ KEY VERSE: 1:18-19
  - ○ OTHER: 2:1, 8-11, 29
- ■ Any other concepts you want to mark

Examples of *Helping Tools*:

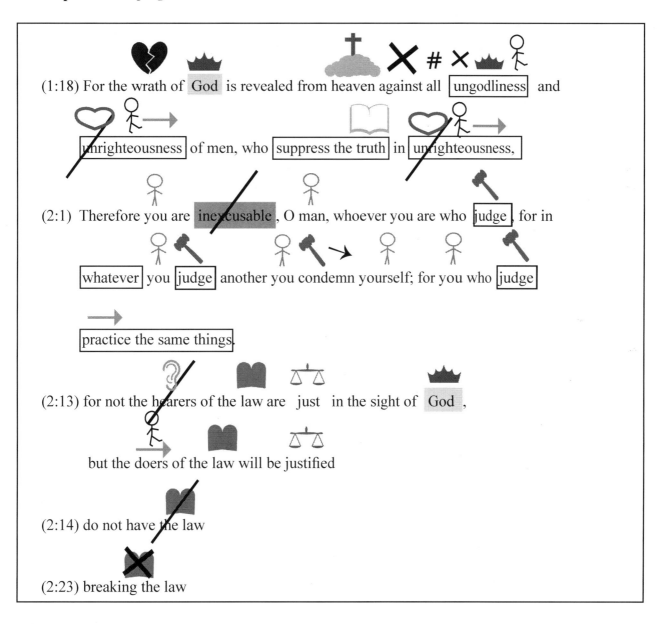

(1:18) For the wrath of God is revealed from heaven against all ungodliness and unrighteousness of men, who suppress the truth in unrighteousness,

(2:1) Therefore you are inexcusable, O man, whoever you are who judge, for in whatever you judge another you condemn yourself; for you who judge practice the same things.

(2:13) for not the hearers of the law are just in the sight of God, but the doers of the law will be justified

(2:14) do not have the law

(2:23) breaking the law

Interpreting the Meaning

Following are questions to help you gain more understanding of the text. As you answer the questions, more questions may arise that you want to explore in the upcoming group session or in your DEVOTION time with God. Feel free to note those here or in your prayer journal.

1. Describe the moral and spiritual condition of the Gentiles.

2. The pagan world's fault was they that suppressed the truth about God revealed in His creation and did not allow it to bear fruit in their lives (1:18-21).

   What characteristics about Himself has the Creator manifested through His creation? What attributes of God do you think about when you experience the natural world around you?

_____

_____

3. Romans 1:23 gives Paul's estimate of idolatry. An idol is an object of worship, such as a statue or a life-controlling force (like power) that takes the place of God. Most likely, Paul knew of particular groups of people whose gods were similar to what he describes in this passage: human beings (the Greeks), animals or birds (the Egyptians) and reptiles (the people of more primitive societies).

What are five modern-day idols that crowd God out of first place in people's lives?

_____

_____

_____

_____

_____

_____

What are four things in your own life that are or could become idols? (Ask for and receive God's forgiveness and help as you explore these.)

_____

_____

_____

_____

4. *Wrath* is a frequent word in Paul's letters (1:18; 2:5, 8; 3:5; 4:15; 5:9). For Paul, this term is not an indication of an outburst of rage, retaliation, or vengefulness on God's part. In 1:21, 24, 28-31, one can get a sense of what God's wrath might look like in this life. We see in these passages how if we are not living in God's light and relying on His wisdom, we make faulty, self-destructive choices and form habits that lead us down a dark road. Walking in such darkness, we are living in God's displeasure.

What do you think the term wrath of God means?

_____

_____

_____

_____

_____

_____

5. Paul indicates that the way God expressed His wrath toward those who continued in: their denial of God's truth (1:18), disrespect for God (becoming dark and unwise in their thinking) (v. 21-22), pursuit of dishonorable passions (v. 24), and worship of other gods (v. 25) was to allow them to pursue their harmful desires and to plunge deeper and deeper into their sins. Paul states that God gave them up/gave them over to their desires (1:24, 26, 28).

What do you think the phrases "gave them up" and "gave them over" mean? List the things to which Paul says God gave them up/gave them over.

_____

_____

_____

_____

_____

6. The annual Hebrew Day of Atonement included the confession of twenty-two sins, one for each letter of the Hebrew alphabet. Whether intentionally or not, in 1:24-32 Paul lists twenty-two vices, though they are not in the order of the Hebrew alphabet. These vices are intended as the judgment and wrath of God, the natural consequences of abandoning Him and His ways, and the beginning of death. This grim picture is supported by non-Christian writers in Paul's day. The twenty-two vices can be easily classified in three areas: idolatry (1:24-25), sensuality (1:26-27), and social strife (1:27-31).

Considering these three categories, list six vices that you think are most prevalent today and comment on each one.

_____

_____

_____

_____

_____

7. Paul teaches that the human body is sacred and is the temple of both the human personality and the Holy Spirit (1 Cor. 6:19). Sensuality outside of God's plan for marriage and any form of lust dishonors and violates the sacredness of that temple. Paul notes that the practice of homosexuality is clearly contrary to God's will (Rom. 1:27). What should be the position of the church and Christians on homosexuality and on same-sex marriage in light of the Scripture?

    _____

    _____

    _____

    _____

    _____

    _____

8. In Romans 2:1, Paul turns to address to the Jews, especially the ones who had set themselves up as moral critics of other people (whom Paul refers to as Gentiles).

    Why do you think that the Jews' covenantal relationship with God gave them greater responsibility and greater guilt?

    _____

    _____

    _____

    _____

Why could the same be true for Christians today?

_____

_____

_____

_____

9. What is your understanding of "the law written in their hearts" (2:15)? Relate your answer to this principle: All people will be judged by what God has made available.

_____

_____

_____

_____

_____

_____

10. In 1:32, Paul accused the Gentiles of practicing, approving, and encouraging others to do evil, probably because if others joined in their sins, it would make them feel better.

According to 2:1, were the Jews guilty because they judged others or because they were guilty of doing the same things in a literal sense?

_____

_____

_____

_____

_____

_____

According to 2:4, did the Jews of whom Paul speaks (and even people today), because they were enjoying God's blessings of goodness, forbearance, and longsuffering, presume that they had no need of repentance and trusting in Christ? Perhaps you once struggled with this or have encountered a person with such struggles. In light of Paul's letter, explain what our response to God's blessings should be.

_____

_____

_____

_____

_____

11. Paul has spoken of the wrath of God as being present now (1:18). Romans 2:5 refers to it as occurring in the future in the Final Judgment. Though the Final Judgment is yet to come in its fullness, Paul sees it as already beginning. Can you explain this? (You may find help in Arrington's discussion of the two ages in his commentary, pages 45-46.)

_____

_____

_____

12. Modifying the dark picture of 1:18-32, Paul observes that some Jews and Gentiles have sought glory, honor, peace, immortality, and have done good (2:7, 10). Why is it that a person who responds in this way is responding to the gospel and to the saving work of the Holy Spirit? Note how the conclusion of this chapter (2:26-29) affirms this interpretation.

_____

_____

_____

_____

13. Paul explains the relationship of the Gentiles to the law. In the Final Judgment, the Jews will be judged by the Mosaic law which they had received, but the Gentiles who did not have the Mosaic law will face the Final Judgment on the basis of the law written in their hearts.

How do you understand the law that God has implanted in each person's heart, and how does the law in the heart relate to conscience? (See 2:14-15.)

_____

_____

_____

_____

_____

_____

_____

14. According to Paul, when humans stand before God in the Final Judgment, on what grounds will they receive a favorable verdict?

_____

_____

_____

_____

_____

_____

15. In 2:17-24, Paul speaks to the Jews about their advantages and failures. First, list six of their advantages, and then four areas in which they had failed.

_____

_____

_____

_____

_____

16. Paul has shown that both Jews and Gentiles are in need of salvation. In 2:25-29, Paul argues that circumcision brings responsibility as well as privileges and that keeping the law is beneficial only if the whole law is kept. It might be assumed that by perfect observance of the law, one could earn

salvation, but Romans 3:20 and 7:7-25 show that perfect observance of the law is impossible. Explain the way Paul defines "true circumcision" and a "true Jew." (See Arrington's commentary, pages 98-99.)

_____

_____

_____

_____

_____

_____

_____

Pulling It All Together

Core focus and major themes. Look over Romans 1:18–2:29 once again noticing the *Helping Tools* that you have applied to the text. In the text, mark or note major themes in a way that is helpful to you; maybe make notations in the margin of the text.

In the following table, list at least one core focus for this passage, other major themes you have identified, and what this passage reveals about God's nature.

Summary. Now that you have used *Helping Tools* and answered the questions above to explore and discern the meaning of the text, briefly summarize your own interpretation—what you think Paul is saying in the text.

Core Focus	
Major Themes	
Nature of God	

My Interpretation

_____

_____

_____

_____

_____

DEVOTE

Following your exploration of the meaning of the passage, take a few moments to reflect on what you have discerned, and talk to God about it.

☐ Invite God to use His Word to change you in any way He desires and to direct you in how you might apply His Word to your life.

☐ Consider writing in a journal or notebook your prayers, inspirations, or any decisions that you make during this time with God.

Pause for Prayer

"But glory, honor, and peace to everyone who works what is good, to the Jew first and also to the Greek" *(Romans 2:10).*

Lord, You are holy. You are good. You are honorable. One day, Your righteous judgment will be revealed, and You will honor Your people.

I seek You and Your will. I ask You to pour Your light and life into my heart.

I want to live a holy life and to reflect Your goodness in all that I am and in all that I say and do. Help me to place my hope in You and Your promise of glory, honor, peace, and eternal life.

For Reflection & Prayer

☐ In this passage of Scripture, Paul discussed sin and the outcomes of sin. Did reading this passage impact how you want to approach your own spiritual life and relationship with God? Are there any areas of your life that you want to submit to God for His grace and healing? Talk to God about what is on your heart.

☐ Romans 2:25-29 contains great wisdom about what salvation and a relationship with God really involves. To fully experience Paul's teachings and apply them to your own life, substitute the phrases "baptism in water" for "circumcision," "God's will" for "law," and "Christian" for "Jew":

> "For [**baptism**] is indeed profitable if you keep [**God's will**]; but if you are a breaker of [**God's will**], your [**baptism in water**] has become [**unbaptism**]. Therefore, if an [**unbaptized**] man keeps the righteous requirements of [**God's will**], will not his [**unbaptism**] be counted as [**baptism**]? And will not the physically [**unbaptized**], if he fulfills [**God's will**], judge you who, even with your written code and [**water baptism**],

are a transgressor of [**God's will**]? For he is not a [**Christian**] who is one outwardly, nor is [**baptism**] that which is outward in the flesh; but he is a [**Christian**] who is one inwardly; and [**baptism**] is that of the heart, in the Spirit, not in the letter; whose praise is not from men but from God."

☐ Considering the intent of Paul's words in verses 25-29, do you feel the Holy Spirit inspiring you to shift in any way your perception of your own salvation or your approach to your relationship with God?

☐ Meditate on Romans 2:7, 10 (quoted above under the *Pause for Prayer*). Consider how your good actions can be truly good only when they come from God's love within your heart.

☐ Are there any areas of your life (habits, decisions, thoughts, or questions) that have been barriers to your fully experiencing the love of God or expressing His love in the world?

- Give those areas to God, and receive His love and forgiveness.

- Ask and allow Jesus Christ to heal your heart and mind, and set you free.

- Tell Jesus that you want to live saved and free from darkness and to travel through life with Him.

- Ask for the Holy Spirit's guidance and empowerment in changing any habits, moving forward, and living an abundant life in God's truth and goodness.

DISCIPLE

Consider how you might apply to your daily life what you have been learning and experiencing with God during your study of this passage of Scripture.

Living and Sharing Your Faith

"For not the hearers of the law are just in the sight of God, but the doers of the law will be justified" (Romans 2:13).

☐ What truths in Romans 1:18 – 2:29 have impacted you most? How have they affected the way you think or live?

☐ How might you and your church reflect God's healing presence to people trapped in the sins that Paul addresses in this letter?

☐ Talk to your Heavenly Father about any feelings, desires, thoughts, or specific ideas you might have for putting into action the love He has placed in your heart.

☐ Are there any commitments that you feel God is leading you to make at this time?

☐ Is there any specific action you would like to take in response to what you have learned during your time in God's Word this week? Ask the Holy Spirit to help you, and take one small step in the direction that you feel Him leading you.

A Closing Prayer

Key Verse:

"For the wrath of God is revealed from heaven against all ungodliness and unrighteousness of men, who suppress the truth in unrighteousness, because what may be known of God is manifest in them, for God has shown it to them." (Romans 1:18-19).

Father God, You show us who You are. Your love is everywhere.

You love us so intensely that You are displeased with any darkness that separates us from You and the goodness You desire for us.

Forgive me for allowing sin and carelessness to interfere with our relationship.

I ask You to help me live in your truth and goodness, and reflect to others the love You have placed in my heart through Your Spirit.

Thank You for Your forgiveness and the life You offer me!

ENLIVEN
ENCOUNTERING GOD
through
HIS WORD

LESSON FOUR

Romans

CHAPTERS 3:1-31

ALL PEOPLE EQUAL IN THEIR NEED OF SALVATION

LESSON FOUR

ROMANS: 3:1-31

ALL PEOPLE EQUAL IN THEIR NEED OF SALVATION

Key Verse

"What then? Are we better than they? Not at all. For we have previously charged both Jews and Greeks that they are all under sin. As it is written: 'There is none righteous, no, not one'" (Romans 3:9-10).

Introduction

In chapter 2 of Romans, Paul has contended that the work of the Holy Spirit in the lives of the Gentiles had made them true Jews—people in a right relationship with God. He has also asserted that true circumcision is a matter of the heart. Chapter 3 opens with two questions: (1) Is there any advantage to being a Jew by natural decent, and (2) Is there any profit to physical circumcision? Paul's previous discussion in Romans 2 seems to lead to the conclusion that there is no advantage where salvation is concerned. Even so, in light of the teaching of the Old Testament and God's covenant with and faithfulness to the Jewish people, they could not be considered to be the same as other nations.

Paul's question–answer technique. As is characteristic of Paul's teaching style, he enters into dialogue with an imaginary opponent. This style is known as a *diatribe* (a discourse), in which Paul uses a question and answer technique. Previously during his missionary journeys, Paul had encountered fellow Jews who expressed opposition to his message. From these encounters, he knew the types of questions that his Jewish opponents would normally have regarding the gospel. To identify the opponent's questions, read 3:1, 3, 5, 7. Paul's answers are found in 3:2, 4, 6, 8, 9-18. Some of Paul's answers may not seem complete, but he will pick up some of the issues and answer them more fully later. The diatribe technique appears elsewhere in Paul's letter, especially in chapters 10 and 11.

Equal before God. The chief advantage of the Jews was that they possessed the oracles of God, namely the Hebrew Scriptures of the Old Testament, the law. Having conceded that the Jews have an advantage (3:2; see also 9:4-5), Paul insists that the Jews and Gentiles stand as equals before God. Whatever advantages the Jews had, these advantages alone could not save them, because all humans (Jews and Gentiles) are under the dominion of sin (3:9). To show that all persons without exception are sinners, the Apostle brings together six passages from the Psalms and one from Isaiah (Ps. 14:1-3; 53:1-3; 5:9; 140:3; 10:7; Isa. 59:7-8; Ps. 36:1). All people are in the same situation—all need a Savior.

Righteousness through faith. Both Jews and Gentiles were under the power of sin, but Paul speaks about a great turning point in God's revelation of His relationship with people and provision for their salvation: "But now the righteousness of God apart from the law is revealed…" (3:21). Here "righteousness" does not refer to the character of God or to human virtues bestowed by God, but to God's saving initiative in the death and resurrection of Christ. Manifested in the law, righteousness leads to wrath and condemnation of sinners (God's displeasure and a guilty verdict due to violation of the law), but in the context of Christ's death on the cross, righteousness is God's delivering activity through Christ. This righteousness sets the believer free from condemnation by the law, and it establishes a right relationship between God and the believer. This right standing and relationship with God is received by the believer through faith and faith alone.

God as divine justice & God as divine love. Romans 3:21-26 is one of the most important passages in Paul's letter, but it is difficult to interpret because Paul struggles with both God as a demanding Judge (divine justice) and God as a forgiving, merciful Father (divine love). His conclusion is that the cross is the answer because through Jesus Christ's death on the cross, He took our place, bearing the penalty for humankind's wrongdoings, and meeting the demands of divine justice. God is, therefore, merciful and forgiving without treating sin lightly. Through the cross, God's justice and love were reconciled. As Paul indicates, God shows His righteousness (His righteous character) by being both just and the justifier of whoever has faith in Jesus Christ (v. 26). Observe that Paul emphasizes the importance of faith in Romans 3:22, 25, 26, 30, 31.

At the end of this chapter in verses 27-31, Paul returns to his diatribe pattern, asserting three points from his previous discussions: (1) No grounds exist for boasting, since the way to God is through faith alone. (2) The way to God is the same for all people. (3) Justification by faith does not render the law useless.

Your Exploration of the Text

Pause for Prayer

"Therefore no one will be declared righteous in God's sight by the works of the law; rather, through the law we become conscious of our sin. But now apart from the law the righteousness of God has been made known, to which the Law and the Prophets testify. This righteousness is given through faith in Jesus Christ to all who believe." (Romans 3:20-22, NIV).

Father, You are righteous and holy.

You gave Your law and the teachings of Your prophets to help Your people live a righteous and holy life.

Even though we have faltered in our self-discipline and efforts to keep Your laws,
You have taken compassion on us, and through your Son Jesus, You have delivered us from our sins and weaknesses. There is no other god like You!

I pray that as I study Your Word, You will reveal to my heart—

my need for deliverance from any sinful habits, which the law reveals, and

my need to believe and embrace Your gracious plan for my salvation,

which You offer me through faith in Your Son Jesus Christ.

THE TEXT

Romans 3:1-31

[1] What advantage then has the Jew, or what is the profit of circumcision? [2] Much in every way! Chiefly

because to them were committed the oracles of God. [3] For what if some did not believe? Will their

unbelief make the faithfulness of God without effect? [4] Certainly not! Indeed, let God be true but

every man a liar. As it is written:

"That You may be justified in Your words,

And may overcome when You are judged."

[5] But if our unrighteousness demonstrates the righteousness of God, what shall we say? Is God unjust who inflicts wrath? (I speak as a man.) [6] Certainly not! For then how will God judge the world?

[7] For if the truth of God has increased through my lie to His glory, why am I also still judged as a sinner? [8] And why not say, "Let us do evil that good may come"?—as we are slanderously reported and as some affirm that we say. Their condemnation is just.

[9] What then? Are we better than they? Not at all. For we have previously charged both Jews and Greeks that they are all under sin.

[10] As it is written:

"There is none righteous, no, not one;

[11] There is none who understands;

There is none who seeks after God.

[12] They have all turned aside;

They have together become unprofitable;

There is none who does good, no, not one."

[13] "Their throat is an open tomb;

With their tongues they have practiced deceit";

"The poison of asps is under their lips";

[14] "Whose mouth is full of cursing and bitterness."

[15] "Their feet are swift to shed blood;

[16] Destruction and misery are in their ways;

[17] And the way of peace they have not known."

[18] "There is no fear of God before their eyes."

[19] Now we know that whatever the law says, it says to those who are under the law, that every mouth

may be stopped, and all the world may become guilty before God. [20] Therefore by the deeds of the law

no flesh will be justified in His sight, for by the law is the knowledge of sin.

[21] But now the righteousness of God apart from the law is revealed, being witnessed by the Law and

the Prophets, [22] even the righteousness of God, through faith in Jesus Christ, to all and on all who believe. For there is no difference; [23] for all have sinned and fall short of the glory of God, [24] being justified freely by His grace through the redemption that is in Christ Jesus, [25] whom God set forth as a propitiation by His blood, through faith, to demonstrate His righteousness, because in His forbearance God had passed over the sins that were previously committed, [26] to demonstrate at the present time His righteousness, that He might be just and the justifier of the one who has faith in Jesus.

[27] Where is boasting then? It is excluded. By what law? Of works? No, but by the law of faith. [28] Therefore we conclude that a man is justified by faith apart from the deeds of the law. [29] Or is He the God of the Jews only? Is He not also the God of the Gentiles? Yes, of the Gentiles also, [30] since there

is one God who will justify the circumcised by faith and the uncircumcised through faith. [31] Do we

then make void the law through faith? Certainly not! On the contrary, we establish the law.

DISCOVER

Keeping in mind the prayer you have just prayed, begin your exploration of Romans chapter 3, observing the text and discovering the facts.

Observing the Text

Helping Questions. Read carefully Romans chapter 3. As you are moving through your reading of the biblical text, create some *Helping Questions* to help you discover the text. As you create your *Helping Questions*, answer the ones you can, and make quick notes about any questions you want to explore later or any insights that begin to surface.

My Helping Questions and Answers:

_____

_____

_____

_____

Observations. Briefly summarize your discoveries, what you have observed so far by using *Helping Questions.*

My Findings:

_____

_____

_____

_____

_____

_____

DISCERN

Now that you have observed the text and discovered some facts, it is time to take a closer look, to explore the meaning of what Paul is communicating in this section of his letter to the Romans.

Marking the Text

Helping Tools. Go through the passage once again applying *Helping Tools*, using TOOLS that you have already used and creating new ones as needed.

Tips for marking the text:

☐ **Checking your master list of** *Helping Tools*. As you work through the key concepts, be sure to check your master list of the *Helping Tools* that you have been using. It will be helpful to be consistent in the way you mark the text.

☐ **Marking synonyms using the same symbol**. In examining the biblical text, look for both repeated terms and repeated concepts. Paul may repeat a concept, but use a different term to describe that concept. Marking synonyms with the same symbol will help you interpret the meaning.

☐ **Marking Paul's comments about Gentiles and Jews**. In 1:18 – 2:29, Paul talked about both the Gentiles and the Jews. In 3:1-20, he continues writing about the Jews. Be sure to mark this passage like you did the passage about the Jews in LESSON THREE.

☐ **Marking Paul's diatribe**. Using your colored pencils or markers, mark with [brackets] the elements of the discourse method Paul uses in this passage. See the Scripture passages listed below under "Key concepts."

[Jewish opponents' questions]—*bracket in one color*

[Paul's answers]—*bracket in another color*

Key concepts:

- Concepts mentioned in this passage for which you already created *Helping Tools* in previous lessons
- Righteousness of God and people:
  - God's saving, justifying activity in Christ, bringing people into right relationship with Him (justification)—*righteousness* (3:21-25)
- Righteousness of people:
  - Unrighteousness, unholiness in heart and life—*unrighteousness, none righteous…* (3:5, 10-12)
- Speech—o*racles, speak, tongues, mouth, boasting… ***TIP**: Mark speech with a conversation bubble. To indicate godly or neutral talk, leave the bubble empty. To indicate sinful talk, darken in the bubble.
- Sin, evil, sinner
- The law
- Judgment—*judge, condemnation* (legal terms)
- Justice—*just, unjust, justifier, justify/ justified*—granted a right, holy, righteous standing with God through faith (legal terms)

- Redemption
- God/People
- Righteousness of God:
  - God's holiness—*righteousness* (3:5, 26)
- Propitiation (atoning sacrifice)
- Faith/Deeds
- Miscellaneous:
  - Diatribe: **TIP**: Bracket in different colors: [Jewish opponents' questions] (3:1, 3, 5, 7, 27a, 27c-d, 29a-b, 31a) [Paul's answers] (3:2, 4, 6, 8, 9-18, 27b, 27e-28, 29c-30, 31b)
  - Paul's rhetorical questions (**TIP:** They are included in his answers in the diatribe.)
  - Numbers or amounts
  - Indications of time
  - Comparisons, contrasts, repetitions, or progressions and sequences: EXAMPLES: COMPARISON—*throat is an open tomb* (3:13). CONTRAST—*truth of God/my lie* (3:7)
  - One or more focus verses
- Other concepts or terms you want to mark

Interpreting the Meaning

Following are questions to help you gain more understanding of the text. As you answer the questions, more questions may arise that you want to explore in the upcoming group session or in your DEVOTION time with God. Feel free to note those here or in your prayer journal.

1. Romans 3:1-18 is best understood as a dialogue between Paul and an imaginary opponent. Define what a *diatribe* is.

    _____

    _____

    _____

    _____

    _____

    _____

    _____

2. In 3:2, Paul has identified that the biggest advantage that the Jews had was that they possessed the Old Testament, the law. What other advantages do Christians have?

    _____

    _____

    _____

    _____

    _____

3. Paul develops his topic of God's faithfulness in chapters 9–11. What does Paul think of the question in 3:3?

_____

_____

_____

_____

_____

4. In light of the universal fact of sin, compare sin to the disease of cancer.

_____

_____

_____

_____

_____

5. In 3:10-18, Paul cites the Old Testament in order to show the human condition without Christ as Savior. Describe in your own words the sinfulness of every human being in terms of the following:

Human Character (vs. 11-12) _____

_____

_____

_____

Human Speech (vs. 13-15)   _____

_____

_____

_____

_____

Human Conduct (vs. 16-18)   _____

_____

_____

_____

6. In 3:20, Paul clearly teaches that the Mosaic law gives us a knowledge of sin, making us aware of right and wrong. He also emphasizes that the religious rules and regulations of the law have no power to save us from sin and bring us into a right relationship with God. Memorize Romans 3:20, and explain why no one can be saved by simply knowing what is right.

_____

_____

_____

_____

_____

_____

_____

_____

7. Doing things that Christians normally do—carrying the Bible, singing hymns, quoting Scripture, raising hands in church services, or taking communion—none of these actions will deliver you from your sin and God's judgment. Explain why this is true.

_____

_____

_____

_____

_____

8. Why is it that every mouth is silenced before God, and the whole world stands guilty in His presence (3:19)? Considering the context of 3:19, does this guilt apply to each individual person? Explain.

_____

_____

_____

_____

9. In 3:21-22, the phrase "the righteousness of God" is not referring to the character of God, but to the favorable verdict of God in forgiving the sins of those who have faith in Christ. Do you agree or disagree that the phrase "righteousness of God" refers to justification by faith? In answering, consider the context. Note Paul's emphasis on faith and what he has previously said about the righteousness of God.

_____

_____

_____

_____

10. In Romans 3:24-25, Paul endeavors to use language that describes the saving process. (For help understanding this process, see the appendix: "God's Plan of Salvation" in this *Discovery Guide*.)

To focus his discussion on salvation through the cross, Paul uses three significant terms:

(1) Justified (noun, justification)—This is a legal term from the court of law. The picture is that of a guilty criminal coming into a court and being acquitted and released by the judge. When the sinner comes before God with repentance and faith in Christ, the sinner leaves God's court as a free person.

(2) Redemption—A term borrowed from the institution of slavery, redemption was used to describe the process through which someone purchased a slave's freedom. Christ gave Himself as a sin offering and God accepted it as full payment for our sins.

(3) Propitiation—Comes from the practice of animal sacrifice and indicates that Christ's sacrifice blots out the sins of those who put their faith in Him, turning away God's wrath, His displeasure.

Two questions:

(1) Which of these terms has the most significance for you and why?

_____

_____

_____

_____

_____

(2) Have you ever heard someone describe his or her conversion experience, starting with "It was like...," perhaps comparing it to one of the images described above or using some other comparison? Explain.

_____

_____

_____

_____

11. Paul sees the spiritual condition of all people as the same, including both Jews and Gentiles. In 3:23, the phrase "the glory of God" may mean either "God's saving presence" (GNT) or "the beauty of God's plan" (PHILLIPS). Does either fit the context better? If so, why?

_____

_____

_____

_____

_____

12. Romans 3:27-31 returns to the diatribe. These verses repeat some of the points that Paul has already made. Since verse 28 is it significant, you might want to memorize it. In the text, find Paul's answers to his opponent. (You most likely placed those in brackets when you were applying *Helping Tools*.) Briefly write Paul's answers in your own words.

_____

_____

_____

_____

13. What does Paul mean by his statement that through faith we establish the law (v. 31)?

_____

_____

_____

_____

Pulling It All Together

Core focus and major themes. Look over Romans chapter 3 once again noticing the *Helping Tools* that you have applied to the text. In the text, mark or note major themes in a way that is helpful to you.

In the following table, list at least one core focus for this passage, other major themes you have identified, and what this passage reveals about God's nature.

Core Focus:	
Major Themes	
Nature of God:	

Summary. Briefly summarize your own interpretation—what you think Paul is saying in the text.

My Interpretation

_____

_____

_____

_____

_____

_____

_____

_____

_____

_____

DEVOTE

Following your exploration of the meaning of the passage, take a few moments to reflect on what you have discerned, and talk to God about it.

☐ Invite God to use His Word to change you in any way He desires and to direct you in how you are to apply His Word to your life.

☐ Consider writing in a journal or notebook your prayers, inspirations, or any decisions that you make during this time with God.

Pause for Prayer

"For all have sinned and fall short of the glory of God, and all are justified freely by his grace through the redemption that came by Christ Jesus.
God presented Christ as a sacrifice of atonement, through the shedding of his blood—to be received by faith..." (Romans 3:23-25, NIV).

Father, we all have fallen short of Your will for us. Even though our sins and weaknesses are hard to admit, in Your grace, You want us to confess them to You and ask for Your forgiveness.

Jesus, thank You for Your huge sacrifice for us to provide for our redemption and justification, for willingly suffering extreme pain and death so that we might be healed and set free from our sinful inclinations and the prisons that they create for us.

Lord, I pray today asking for You to forgive me for all the times I have fallen short of Your perfect will. Help me humbly accept Your forgiveness for the things I have done and the things I have left undone. Help me to receive the forgiveness You offer me now, and put my trust in You and Your love.

For Reflection & Prayer

☐ How does knowing that Jesus sacrificed His life to redeem you (to purchase your freedom), to be a propitiation for you (to atone for your sins by substituting Himself in order to turn away God's displeasure), and to justify you (to pardon you and set you free without guilt) make you feel about Him? How does it make you feel about your life? Take a few moments to tell Jesus how you feel.

☐ In looking back over your notes in this lesson, is there anything else you would like to say to God?

DISCIPLE

Consider how you might apply to your daily life what you have been learning and experiencing with God during your study of this passage of Scripture.

Living and Sharing Your Faith

"Therefore we conclude that a man is justified by faith apart from the deeds of the law." ... "Do we then make void the law through faith? Certainly not! On the contrary, we establish the law" (Romans 3:28, 31).

☐ What truths in Romans 3:1-31 have impacted you most? How have they affected the way you think or live?

☐ Do you find that your own faith helps you keep the law of God?

☐ Is there any decision you would like to make or action you would like to take that would help strengthen your faith in God?

☐ Are there any commitments that you feel God is leading you to make at this time?

☐ Is there any specific action you would like to take in response to what you have learned during your time in God's Word this week? Ask the Holy Spirit to help you, and take one small step in the direction that you feel Him leading you.

A Closing Prayer

Key Verse:

"What then? Are we better than they? Not at all. For we have previously charged both Jews and Greeks that they are all under sin. As it is written: 'There is none righteous, no, not one'" (Romans 3:9-10).

God, You love everyone. You see that we all have sinned, and You want each of us to be set free from our sins.

Help me to see my own weaknesses, my own need for Your salvation, to humble myself before You, and to release judging others.

Help me to go out into the world and treat others with the same grace and favor that You have given to me.

LESSON FIVE

Romans

CHAPTERS 4:1-25

SALVATION THROUGH FAITH / ABRAHAM & DAVID

Lesson Five

Romans: 4:1-25

Salvation through Faith

ABRAHAM & DAVID

Key Verse

For what does the Scripture say? "Abraham believed God, and it was accounted to him for righteousness." ...David also describes the blessedness of the man to whom God imputes righteousness apart from works: "Blessed are those whose lawless deeds are forgiven, and whose sins are covered; Blessed is the man to whom the Lord shall not impute sin." (Romans 4:3, 6-8).

Introduction

Earlier in Romans 3:21-31, Paul set forth the doctrine of justification by faith. He was eager for his readers not to underestimate the importance this doctrine. Now in chapter 4, he points to Abraham and David as prime examples, showing that justification by faith is scriptural. As Paul has said, the gospel establishes (upholds and fulfills) the law (the Old Testament), but not the religion of salvation through works (3:20, 31). Earlier Paul has observed that both the Old Testament law and prophets had testified of God's saving righteousness that He would bring through the gospel. So having discussed that faith alone leads to justification, the Apostle turns to Abraham and David to illustrate this truth (4:1-12).

Abraham and David's faith. Turning to Abraham, Paul takes us back about four thousand years and shows us that the manner in which God has justified a person has always been the same. Based on Genesis 26:5, the Jews believed that Abraham kept all of the law before the law was given by God to Moses. Continuing in the diatribe style, the implication in chapter 4 is that Paul's imaginary Jewish opponent believes that Abraham had obeyed the law perfectly and had earned salvation by doing good works. To answer the opponent, Paul begins by quoting Genesis 15:6: "Abraham believed God, and it was accounted to him for righteousness" (Rom. 4:3). Abraham's exemplary life may have given him grounds for having pride by human standards. Nevertheless, his salvation was not a reward for works that he had done, but it was his trust in God that brought him salvation. He had nothing about which to boast before God; his good works had not earned him special favor in God's sight.

This passage in Genesis 15 is not referring to reward for works done, but to the gift of salvation given to Abraham and to all those who believe. Paul's use of the word "impute" (account) is important, as it indicates what God counts when considering the lives of people. Earlier in Psalm 32:1-2, David used the term, and now Paul quotes him in Romans 4:7-8. In his Psalm, David did not speak about people being rewarded for goodness, but about sinful people being forgiven of their sins.

So determining (counting, calculating) one's righteousness is a matter of grace. Stated another way, it is the same thing as not imputing (not counting) sin. It is God's forgiveness of sin—justification for all who believe.

Circumcision as a sign and seal of salvation through faith. Abraham received the gift of forgiveness through faith in God. Another fact points to this truth: Abraham was justified before he was circumcised. God accepted Abraham before he received the physical mark of circumcision (Rom. 4:9-12). Abraham's faith and justification are mention in Genesis 15:6, but his circumcision is not mentioned until Genesis 17:10. The patriarch had entered into a right relationship with God about fifteen years before receiving the rite of circumcision. Therefore, circumcision was not instrumental in justifying Abraham before God, but it was the act of faith that made him right with God. Circumcision came after he believed, as a sign and seal of what God had done by receiving him into his family. God forgave Abraham of his sins apart from works, including circumcision. Only those who follow Abraham's example are truly the sons and daughters of God.

God's saving grace. Paul follows the story about Abraham with the testimony of David, Israel's greatest king, who testified to the same truth. Abraham was a man known among the Jews for his religious piety and good works, but David was known as a man who sinned against God and then repented (Ps. 51:1-19; Rom. 4:6-8). The emphasis is on God's refusing to impute (to reckon or count) a person's sins against him. David pronounces a person who receives justifying grace as blessed (Ps. 32:1-2; Rom. 4:7-8), which means that God accepts that person and forgives his or her sins. David knew from experience that God forgives morally bad people who repent of their sins. Both he and

Abraham were dependent on God's saving grace. The truth is that God saves both the morally upright and the morally bad who turn to Him. Apart from Christ, all people, the morally upright and the morally bad, are in need of the Savior.

Definition of faith. Paul has said a lot about faith, but now he proceeds to define it in two ways:

(1) *Faith is the opposite of keeping the law as a sort of contract with God—it is a matter of trusting in God's promise.* If it were a contract, then keeping the contract would earn you salvation. But faith is not a contract. A contract with an employer assures you that if you keep the terms of your side of the agreement, the employer is legally bound to pay you. Salvation is not a matter of contract or of keeping the rules and regulations of the law, but it is a matter of promise and faith. From the biblical account of Abraham, we read that God promised him and his descendants a great blessing (Gen. 22:17-18). The fulfillment of the promise depended on faith, ruling out the earning of salvation by works. If salvation depended on human virtue and deeds, then faith and promise have lost their meaning (Rom. 4:14).

(2) *For a positive definition of faith, Paul appeals again to the story of Abraham, who was known for his great belief and trust in God.* On many occasions, Abraham demonstrated faith in God even when his life circumstances did not seem to support it. In Romans, Paul reminds his readers of the faith that Abraham had late in his life, which led to the birth of Isaac and to Abraham's descendants becoming a great people.

God had promised Abraham many descendants (Gen. 15:4-6; 17:7). In response, Abraham trusted that he could produce children, even though he knew that in himself he did not have the power (Rom. 4:18-21)—due to the fact that he was a hundred years old and his wife Sarah was ninety (Gen. 17:17). From the human standpoint, Abraham's faith went against all logic. At one point, Abraham did have a lapse of faith when he fathered a child with Hagar, his wife Sarah's maid (Gen. 16:1-6). Later, however, when God reminded Abraham of His divine plan, he turned once again to rely on God's power instead of his own (Gen. 17:15-21, 24). Abraham looked again to the Creator who is able to raise the dead and create things out of nothing (Rom. 4:17). Just as God had promised, Isaac was born to Sarah and Abraham.

Our faith and salvation. As Paul indicates, the remarks said about Abraham also apply to us (4:23-25). Justification by faith is a universal truth. If we believe in the power of God as Abraham did, God credits (or imputes) our faith to us as righteousness—a short way of saying God forgives our sins and brings us into a right relationship with Himself. Isaac's birth to elderly parents demonstrates to us God's power to create and bring life into the world, but it also illustrates for us the nature of God's power at work in the death and resurrection of Jesus. As C. K. Barrett has said, "God's power did not raise His Son from a dead womb, but from a grave in which they had buried Him" (*A Commentary on the Epistle to the Romans*, Harper & Row, 1957, p. 99). Our faith is anchored in the Creator and Life-Giver, just as Abraham's was.

Your Exploration of the Text

Pause for Prayer

"Therefore, the promise comes by faith, so that it may be by grace and may be guaranteed to all Abraham's offspring—not only to those who are of the law but also to those who have the faith of Abraham. He is the father of us all." (Romans 4:16, NIV)

Father, through Your grace, You promise eternal life to all Abraham's descendants, all who follow in Abraham's footsteps by placing their faith and trust in You.

As I study Paul's teachings about the life of Abraham, help me, too, to put my trust in You and Your promises.

THE TEXT

Romans 4:1-25

[1] What then shall we say that Abraham our father has found according to the flesh? [2] For if Abraham was justified by works, he has something to boast about, but not before God. [3] For what does the

Scripture say? "Abraham believed God, and it was accounted to him for righteousness." [4] Now to him

who works, the wages are not counted as grace but as debt.

[5] But to him who does not work but believes on Him who justifies the ungodly, his faith is accounted

for righteousness, [6] just as David also describes the blessedness of the man to whom God imputes

righteousness apart from works:

[7] "Blessed are those whose lawless deeds are forgiven,

And whose sins are covered;

[8] Blessed is the man to whom the Lord shall not impute sin."

[9] Does this blessedness then come upon the circumcised only, or upon the uncircumcised also? For

we say that faith was accounted to Abraham for righteousness. [10] How then was it accounted? While

he was circumcised, or uncircumcised? Not while circumcised, but while uncircumcised. [11] And he

received the sign of circumcision, a seal of the righteousness of the faith which he had while still

uncircumcised, that he might be the father of all those who believe, though they are uncircumcised,

that righteousness might be imputed to them also, [12] and the father of circumcision to those who not

only are of the circumcision, but who also walk in the steps of the faith which our father Abraham

had while still uncircumcised.

[13] For the promise that he would be the heir of the world was not to Abraham or to his seed through the

law, but through the righteousness of faith. [14] For if those who are of the law are heirs, faith is made

void and the promise made of no effect, [15] because the law brings about wrath; for where there is no law there is no transgression.

[16] Therefore it is of faith that it might be according to grace, so that the promise might be sure to all the seed, not only to those who are of the law, but also to those who are of the faith of Abraham, who is the father of us all [17] (as it is written, "I have made you a father of many nations") in the presence of Him whom he believed—God, who gives life to the dead and calls those things which do not exist as though they did; [18] who, contrary to hope, in hope believed, so that he became the father of many nations, according to what was spoken, "So shall your descendants be." [19] And not being weak in faith, he did not consider his own body, already dead (since he was about a hundred years old), and the deadness of Sarah's womb. [20] He did not waver at the promise of God through unbelief, but was strengthened in faith, giving glory to God, [21] and being fully convinced that what He had promised He

was also able to perform. [22] And therefore "it was accounted to him for righteousness."

[23] Now it was not written for his sake alone that it was imputed to him, [24] but also for us. It shall be imputed to us who believe in Him who raised up Jesus our Lord from the dead, [25] who was delivered up because of our offenses, and was raised because of our justification.

DISCOVER

Keeping in mind the prayer you have just prayed, begin your exploration of Romans chapter 4, observing the text and discovering the facts.

Observing the Text

Helping Questions. Read carefully Romans chapter 4. As you are moving through your reading of the biblical text, create some *Helping Questions* to help you discover the text.

My Helping Questions and Answers:

_____

_____

_____

_____

_____

_____

_____

_____

_____

_____

_____

Observations. Briefly summarize your discoveries, what you have observed so far by using _Helping Questions._

My Findings:

_____

_____

_____

_____

_____

_____

_____

_____

_____

_____

_____

_____

_____

_____

_____

_____

DISCERN

Now that you have observed the text and discovered some facts, it is time to take a closer look, to explore the meaning of what Paul is communicating in this section of his letter to the Romans.

Marking the Text

Helping Tools. Go through the passage once again applying *Helping Tools*, using TOOLS that you have already used and creating new ones as needed.

Key Concepts

■ Concepts mentioned in this passage for which you have created *Helping Tools* in previous lessons
■ God (members of the Holy Trinity)
■ People-*Abraham, David,* terms and phrases that Paul uses to indicate Jews and Gentiles
■ Righteousness of people:
  • In a right standing with God through faith-*righteousness (4:3, 5, 9, 11, 13, 22)*
■ Justification (being granted a right, holy, righteous standing with God through faith)
■ Faith-*faith, believe* / Works
■ The law
■ Counted as—*accounted, counted, imputed* (business terms)
■ Grace/Debt, wages
	■ God's promise
	■ Miscellaneous
	  • Diatribe:
	   [Jewish opponents' questions] (4:1, 9a, 10a-b)
	   [Paul's answers] (4:2-8, 9b, 10c-12)
	  • Paul's rhetorical question (*TIP: It is included in his answer in the diatribe.)
	  • Numbers or amounts
	  • Indications of time
	  • Comparisons, contrasts, repetitions, or progressions and sequences:
	   Examples:
	   COMPARISON—one's spiritual standing to business/work transactions.
	   REPETITION—account, impute
	■ One or more focus verses

Interpreting the Meaning

Following are questions to help you gain more understanding of the text.

1. In Romans 4:1-12, the dialogue continues between Paul and an imaginary opponent. First, the opponent argues that Abraham was justified by his good works (4:1). Paul's reply is that Abraham

had a right to be proud of his exemplary life by human standards, but he had no basis for pride before God.

a.　List six things in which you have seen individuals take pride.

_____

_____

_____

_____

_____

_____

_____

_____

_____

_____

b.　Underline those in which you yourself have had pride.

c.　Circle any of those that you have been inclined to think would earn you points toward God's saving favor.

d.　Now take a moment to look over your list and pray. Give each matter of pride to God. Ask for His forgiveness, receive His love and grace, and pray that He will bless others. Thank God for His gift of grace that no one can earn.

2. Paul's quote in 4:3 is from Genesis 15:6; it is the scriptural foundation for Paul's belief that God's relationship with Israel has always been a faith relationship. Explain why this is true. Keep in mind Abraham, the father of the nation of Israel.

_____

_____

_____

_____

_____

3. In 4:3-4, Paul draws a sharp contrast between wages and the gift of grace. How does salvation, which cannot be earned as wages, fit into Paul's argument? Explain.

_____

_____

_____

_____

_____

4. Paul has lifted up Abraham as an example of religious piety, a piety that, alone without faith, could not earn salvation for Abraham. Paul also refers to the testimony of the great king David. What is the lesson that Paul is teaching by appealing to the words of David recorded in Psalm 32:1-2?

_____

_____

_____

_____

_____

_____

_____

_____

5. In 4:9-10, the opponent's questions about circumcision and "this blessedness" concern how circumcision relates to forgiveness. Does God treat the circumcised and the uncircumcised the same?

_____

_____

_____

_____

_____

_____

In your own words, explain how Paul answers these questions, noting that the Apostle thinks that it is more important to think of Abraham as the father of people of faith rather than as the father of a nation of circumcised people (4:10-12).

_____

_____

_____

_____

_____

_____

6. What is the significance of the fact that nothing is said about circumcision when Abraham believed in the Lord (was saved) (Genesis 15:6), then after Abraham had been in a right relationship with God for about fifteen or twenty years, Abraham then received the mark of circumcision as a sign of his salvation (Gen. 17:9-11, 24)?

_____

_____

_____

_____

_____

_____

_____

7. Thinking now as a Christian, do you see any connection between your water baptism and the practice of circumcision in the Old Testament? Explain. (You may want see Arrington's commentary, pages 100, 128-29.)

_____

_____

_____

_____

_____

_____

8. In 4:13, Paul addresses the erroneous understanding that God's promises make Him indebted to us (or using a common expression, put God in the red). It is not possible for us to live in such a way to make God indebted to us, obligating Him to pay us off. The real truth is that the fulfillment of God's promises to us depends on our faith in the faithfulness of God.

   Why is it that the law is unable to determine the heirs of salvation? Note what 4:14-15 says about how the law disqualifies us as heirs of salvation. Explain.

   _____

   _____

   _____

   _____

   _____

   _____

9. Paul returns to the story of Abraham to emphasize that God is able to do the impossible. He presents the magnitude of Abraham's faith—"who, contrary to hope, in hope believed" (4:18). The phrase "contrary to hope, in hope" literally means "beyond hope, in hope." The first mention of the word

hope here refers to human hope, indicating that when human hope is exhausted, God given hope, which always looks to God, comes into play.

From a human point of view, explain why things looked so bleak for Abraham.

_____

_____

_____

_____

_____

10. The quotation in 4:18 is only part of the story of Abraham. According to Genesis 15:5, God told Abraham to look at the stars of heaven that cannot be numbered. Then He added, "So shall your descendants be." Explain how this promise was fulfilled and is still being fulfilled.

_____

_____

_____

_____

_____

11. Romans 4:20-21 is a good definition of faith. Underline these verses and memorize them to help you firmly plant in your mind that you can always put your faith in God, for He always keeps His promises. Rewrite these verses in the following ways:

As a personal prayer and confession of faith that you speak to God:

Lord, You are _____

_____

_____

As a creedal statement of what you believe:

I believe _____

_____

12. Abraham grew impatient and had a child with the Egyptian handmaid, Hagar, a decision of his, which was outside the perfect plan of God (Gen. 16:1-6; Rom. 9:6-9). We know that during this time Abraham's faith was weak.

    Why is it not right to try to accomplish God's purpose in ways that do not include sincere prayer, patient hope, and the leading of the Holy Spirit?

    _____

    _____

    _____

    _____

    _____

    _____

Pulling It All Together

Core focus and major themes. Look over Romans chapter 4 once again noticing the *Helping Tools* that you have applied to the text. In the text, mark or note major themes in a way that is helpful to you.

In the following table, list at least one core focus for this passage, other major themes you have identified, and what this passage reveals about God's nature.

Core Focus:	
Major Themes:	

Nature of God:	

Summary. Briefly summarize your own interpretation—what you think Paul is saying in the text.

My Interpretation

_____

_____

_____

_____

_____

_____

_____

DEVOTE

Following your exploration of the meaning of the passage, take a few moments to reflect on what you have discerned, and talk to God about it.

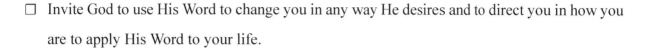

☐ Invite God to use His Word to change you in any way He desires and to direct you in how you are to apply His Word to your life.

☐ Consider writing in a journal or notebook your prayers, inspirations, or any decisions that you make during this time with God.

Pause for Prayer

"The words 'it was credited to him' were written not for him [Abraham] alone, but also for us, to whom God will credit righteousness—for us who believe in him who raised Jesus our Lord from the dead. He was delivered over to death for our sins and was raised to life for our justification" (Romans 4:23-25, NIV).

God, You have blessed us in so many ways, the greatest of which is through Your Son.

You have done so much that we can never repay the debt we owe You. But You tell us that it is already paid through the sacrifice of Jesus our Lord and Savior!

Thank You that when I come to You in faith, You credit my account like You did Abraham's. You set me free from all the penalties for my sins and count me as righteous in Your sight.

For Reflection & Prayer

☐ Take a moment to consider how no religious practice or good deeds can purify us enough to stand in God's holy presence. How does that make you feel? Talk to God about it.

☐ Now consider that through faith we can stand in God's holy presence with confidence and peace because we have been made holy through the sacrifice of our Lord Jesus Christ and our faith-relationship with God. How does that make you feel? Talk to God about your feelings.

☐ In looking back over your notes in this lesson, is there anything else you would like to talk to God about?

DISCIPLE

Consider how you might apply to your daily life what you have been learning and experiencing with God during your study of this passage of Scripture.

Living and Sharing Your Faith

"He [Abraham] did not waver at the promise of God through unbelief, but was strengthened in faith, giving glory to God, and being fully convinced that what He had promised He was also able to perform."(Romans 4:20-21).

☐ What truths in Romans 4:1-25 have impacted you most? How have they affected the way you think or live?

☐ How does knowing that it is your faith, and not your works, that places you in relationship with God affect how you view the good deeds you do? How does this knowledge affect the way you plan to move forward in your life?

☐   Are there any commitments that you feel God is leading you to make at this time?

☐   Is there any specific action you would like to take in response to what you have learned during your time in God's Word this week? Ask the Holy Spirit to help you, and take one small step in the direction that you feel Him leading you.

A Closing Prayer

Key Verse:

"For what does the Scripture say? 'Abraham believed God, and it was accounted to him for righteousness.'" "...David also describes the blessedness of the man to whom God imputes righteousness apart from works: 'Blessed are those whose lawless deeds are forgiven, and whose sins are covered; Blessed is the man to whom the Lord shall not impute sin.'" (Romans 4:3, 6-8).

Thank You, Father, You have blessed us!

You have loved us in the middle of all our weaknesses and struggles.

You have offered us Your gift of righteousness—a right, good, holy standing with You, without requiring us to follow rules, laws, or rituals in order to earn this special place in Your family and kingdom.

Thank You for covering our sins and erasing our debt through the sacrifice and love of our Lord Jesus Christ.

As I go forward, help me to put my faith in You and Your promises of salvation, and to live in the eternal hope I have in You.

LESSON SIX

Romans

CHAPTERS 5:1-21

THE BLESSINGS OF JUSTIFICATION / ADAM & CHRIST

LESSON SIX

ROMANS: 5:1-21

THE BLESSINGS OF JUSTIFICATION

ADAM & CHRIST

Key Verse

For if by the one man's offense death reigned through the one, much more those who receive abundance of grace and of the gift of righteousness will reign in life through the One, Jesus Christ (Romans 5:17).

Introduction

As we move into chapter 5, we will observe that Paul uses a variety of new terms and ideas for the first time in Romans. He has already devoted much time and thought to justification by faith, but now he expands this discussion, recognizing that it is important for his readers to know how they stand with God and the benefits of being in a right relationship with Him. Biblical teaching about justification is just as important for the modern church as it was in Paul's day. Justification by faith is not the only important truth in the Christian life, but our salvation, including heaven itself, depends on it.

Benefits of a right relationship with God. In this passage, Paul introduces four benefits of being in a right relationship with God: (1) peace with God, (2) access to grace, (3) full confidence in a future of sharing in God's glory, (4) and rejoicing during the afflictions of life (5:1-4). These blessings assure us that we have a right standing with God. The hope we have in Christ never disappoints because it rests on God's abundant love that has already been poured out in our hearts by the Holy Spirit. In 5:5, Paul uses the same verb, "poured out," that was used to describe the Holy Spirit's being poured out on the early believers at Pentecost (Acts 2:17) and later, on Cornelius and his friends (10:44). Apparently, Paul is describing the same experience that Pentecostals call *baptism in the Holy Spirit*, which was predicted in Joel 2:28-30. This experience assures believers of God's love, of empowerment by the Holy Spirit, and of their future glory.

Tribulations, perseverance, and hope. Do the suffering and adversities of Christians deny the benefits of justification by faith? No, the Spirit has transformed our hearts and filled us with God's love and power. What God has done for us gives us assurance of the love of God, but the conclusive proof that God loves us is that Christ died for us while we were still sinners (5:8). Then how can we doubt the love of God, especially in light of the supreme demonstration of God's love through the cross? This assurance we have of God's love and the hope that it gives us helps us persevere through life's difficulties.

Justification and Reconciliation. In Romans 5:9-11, Paul emphasizes that through the death of His Son, God has justified and reconciled us to Himself. The important words "reconciled" and "reconciliation" appear here for the first time in Paul's letter to the Romans. As we have noted, the term justification is from the court of law and pictures God as a judge who acquits the guilty. Justification and reconciliation are practically identical, but reconciliation is a term from human relations and always refers to the restoration of friendship between two persons. It pictures us in our sin as rebels against God. When we receive the benefits of the cross by faith, this restores harmony between God and us.

Sin and death/Forgiveness and life. Paul, having looked at the benefits of justification and belief in God's love in the face of suffering, now turns to a much discussed passage that has had a tremendous influence on theology. In Romans 5:12-21, Paul presents Adam as the source of human sin and death, and Christ as the source of forgiveness and life. Both Adam and Christ initially affected the entire human race. They did so in opposite ways: "For as by one man's disobedience many were made sinners, so also by one Man's obedience many will be made righteous" (5:19).

A basic question is: Why are we affected by Adam's sin? In Romans 5:18-19, where Adam's disobedience and Christ's obedience are contrasted, Paul indicates that Adam's sin made all sinners. How is it that all people are held accountable for Adam's rebellion? In trying to answer this question, scholars have proposed four interpretations of Romans 5:12:

1. There is no close connection between Adam's sin and ours. His sin is only typical of ours.

2. We inherit from Adam the tendency to sin and thus it is transmitted from parent to child.

3. Adam was appointed by God as the representative of the whole human race. As a result, we are held accountable for what Adam did.

4. All humankind actually sinned in Adam; when he sinned, Adam and the human race were one since they were in his loins.

(If you want more details on these various views, see Arrington's commentary, pages 149-51.)

We must allow difference of opinion in regard to the interpretation of Romans 5:12. It must not be assumed that because we are automatically condemned (considered guilty) for Adam's sin, that we are automatically saved by Christ's obedience. The obedience of Christ does not relieve us of repenting and believing. Romans 5:18-19 and 1 Corinthians 15:22 should be interpreted in light of the Scriptures in their entirety. Christian doctrine cannot be based on isolated verses and passages of Scripture. The Word of God clearly teaches that God judges a person for his or her sin and that no one is saved apart from repentance and faith.

Adam and Jesus Christ. It is important for you to recognize that in Romans 5:12-21, the magnitude of the saving work of Christ is set against the sin of Adam. Jesus was a man like Adam, and whereas Adam was disobedient, Christ was obedient. On the other hand, Jesus was unlike Adam, for He was not merely a man but God. His obedience was a divine act of grace that leads to justification for those who believe in Him (5:16). The grace that Christ brought did not balance Adam's sin; it overbalanced it. "But where sin abounded, grace abounded much more" (5:20; compare 5:15, 17). The surplus and power of grace in Christ against Adam's transgression makes possible eternal life. Everyone can be sure that God's saving grace is for her or him.

Your Exploration of the Text

Pause for Prayer

"Therefore, as through one man's offense judgment came to all men, resulting in condemnation, even so through one Man's righteous act the free gift came to all men, resulting in justification of life. For as by one man's disobedience many were made sinners, so also by one Man's obedience many will be made righteous" (Romans 5:18-19).

God, You are just, and Your justice is kind and good. In the gracious generosity of Your justice, You sacrificed Your own Son, in order to bring us from a position of death and condemnation due to sin, into a just, holy, righteous place with You and within our spirit.

Thank You for wanting me to be reconciled and to enjoy wonderful fellowship with You.

During this time of study, I ask You to open my mind and heart regarding how I might be obedient to Your plan for me, how I might go about accepting, receiving, and living fully in Your gifts of justification, righteousness, and reconciliation.

THE TEXT

Romans 5:1-21

[1] Therefore, having been justified by faith, we have peace with God through our Lord Jesus Christ, [2]

through whom also we have access by faith into this grace in which we stand, and rejoice in hope of the

glory of God. [3] And not only that, but we also glory in tribulations, knowing that tribulation produces

perseverance; [4] and perseverance, character; and character, hope. [5] Now hope does not disappoint,

because the love of God has been poured out in our hearts by the Holy Spirit who was given to us.

[6] For when we were still without strength, in due time Christ died for the ungodly. [7] For scarcely for

a righteous man will one die; yet perhaps for a good man someone would even dare to die. [8] But God demonstrates His own love toward us, in that while we were still sinners, Christ died for us. [9] Much

more then, having now been justified by His blood, we shall be saved from wrath through Him. [10]

For if when we were enemies we were reconciled to God through the death of His Son, much more,

having been reconciled, we shall be saved by His life. [11] And not only that, but we also rejoice in God

through our Lord Jesus Christ, through whom we have now received the reconciliation.

[12] Therefore, just as through one man sin entered the world, and death through sin, and thus death

spread to all men, because all sinned— [13] (For until the law sin was in the world, but sin is not imputed

when there is no law. [14] Nevertheless death reigned from Adam to Moses, even over those who had

not sinned according to the likeness of the transgression of Adam, who is a type of Him who was to

come. [15] But the free gift is not like the offense. For if by the one man's offense many died, much more the grace of God and the gift by the grace of the one Man, Jesus Christ, abounded to many. [16] And

the gift is not like that which came through the one who sinned. For the judgment which came from

one offense resulted in condemnation, but the free gift which came from many offenses resulted in

justification. [17] For if by the one man's offense death reigned through the one, much more those who

receive abundance of grace and of the gift of righteousness will reign in life through the One, Jesus

Christ.)

[18] Therefore, as through one man's offense judgment came to all men, resulting in condemnation, even

so through one Man's righteous act the free gift came to all men, resulting in justification of life. [19]

For as by one man's disobedience many were made sinners, so also by one Man's obedience many

will be made righteous.

[20] Moreover the law entered that the offense might abound. But where sin abounded, grace abounded much more, [21] so that as sin reigned in death, even so grace might reign through righteousness to eternal life through Jesus Christ our Lord.

DISCOVER

Keeping in mind the prayer you have just prayed, begin your exploration of Romans chapter 5, observing the text and discovering the facts.

Observing the Text

Helping Questions. Read carefully Romans chapter 5. As you are moving through your reading of the biblical text, create some *Helping Questions* to help you discover the text.

My Helping Questions and Answers:

_____

_____

_____

_____

Observations. Briefly summarize your discoveries, what you have observed so far by using *Helping Questions*.

My Findings:

_____

_____

_____

_____

_____

_____

_____

DISCERN

Now that you have observed the text and discovered some facts, it is time to take a closer look, to explore the meaning of what Paul is communicating in this section of his letter to the Romans.

Marking the Text

Helping Tools. Go through the passage once again applying *Helping Tools*, using TOOLS that you have already used and creating new ones as needed.

Key concepts:

- Concepts mentioned in this passage for which you have created *Helping Tools* in previous lessons
- God—Jesus (*one Man*) / People—Adam (*one man*)
- Faith
- Blessings—*peace, grace, hope, love...*
- Tribulations → perseverance → character → hope
- Give, gift / Receive
- Righteousness of God:
  - Jesus Christ's holy, obedient act through the cross—*righteous act* (5:18)
- Righteousness of God and people:
  - God's saving, justifying activity in Christ, bringing people into right relationship with Him – righteousness (5:20-21)
- Righteousness of people:
  - A right, holy standing with God—*gift of righteousness, made righteous* (5:17,19)
  - Holiness of heart and life—*righteous* (5:7)
- Sin → death / Grace → justification → reconciliation → life
  - Comparisons, contrasts, repetitions, or progressions and sequences
  - One or more focus verses
- Miscellaneous:
  - Numbers or amounts
  - Indication of time
- Any other concepts you want to mark

Interpreting the Meaning

Following are questions to help you gain more understanding of the text.

1. Justification by faith brings many blessings. In Romans 5:1-5, Paul identifies four of them: peace, grace, hope, and love. Locate these in the text, and mark them with *Helping Tools* (if you haven't already). Then describe each of these terms in light of your own Christian experience.

    _____

    _____

    _____

    _____

    _____

    _____

2. God's wrath (holy displeasure) is turned toward those who sin. For when we engage in sin, we are going against God and are placing ourselves in the hostile position of an enemy of God's love and goodness. Through faith, when we surrender to Him, we receive His grace and forgiveness, and are reconciled to Him—and come to experience peace.

    What is the difference between peace with God and inner peace? Are they closely related? (See Romans 5:9-10, for help with the answer.)

    _____

    _____

    _____

    _____

    _____

3. What do you think Paul means by, "rejoice in hope of the glory of God" (5:2).

    _____

    _____

    _____

    _____

    _____

4. Times of suffering are times of testing. Suffering reveals whether or not we love God primarily for the things that He provides for us, such as the physical blessings of health, prosperity, and security. When these are no longer available, we learn to be patient, to have fortitude and courage, and to rely on God.

    Record an example of trouble through which you or another person has emerged stronger in Christian character and hope. Also, underline and memorize Romans 5:3-4 to be an encouragement to you in your life.

    _____

    _____

    _____

    _____

    _____

    _____

5. Pentecostals believe that after conversion there is a deeper experience in the love and power of God, called baptism in the Spirit. Many believers have testified that on the occasion that they invited Christ into their lives and accepted His gift of salvation, they experienced God's pouring out His love into their hearts. Then later on, they have experienced baptism in the Spirit, a blessing of a more profound measure of God's love and power, with the sign of speaking in tongues as the believers did at Pentecost (Acts 2).

Can you relate personally with a similar experience like described in Acts 2:1-4, 10:44, and Romans 5:5? Is there a particular time when you have felt the love and power of the Holy Spirit in a special way? Explain.

_____

_____

_____

_____

_____

_____

_____

6. Pentecostal theology declares the power of God to deliver us from trouble and suffering. Faith as small as a mustard seed can remove mountains, heal the sick, and cast out demons (Matt. 17:20; Luke 17:6). These are biblical truths, but sometimes God expects us to climb the mountain, and

He grants us enduring power to do so. Enduring grace is just as miraculous as God instantly lifting a person out of trouble.

Why do you think that at times God delivers us through trouble rather than out of it?

_____

_____

_____

_____

_____

_____

7. The word "for" in Romans 5:6, 8 can be interpreted in two ways: (1) Christ died for our benefit or (2) Christ died in our place. Can you explain the difference between the two interpretations?

_____

_____

_____

_____

_____

_____

Which do you think the Scriptures teach, and which appeals to you?

_____

_____

_____

_____

_____

_____

_____

8. In Romans 5:10-11, Paul introduces the words "reconcile" and "reconciliation." What is the essential difference between justification and reconciliation? List the parallels between the two terms expressed in verses 9 and 10. (For assistance, see the appendix: "God's Plan of Salvation" in this *Discovery Guide*.)

_____

_____

_____

_____

_____

_____

_____

9. Both Adam and Christ affected all people in opposite ways. Read through Romans 5:12-21, and explain how Adam affected everyone for worse and Christ affected everyone for better. As you do this, be aware that the words "all" and "many" are synonyms in this passage.

_____

_____

_____

_____

_____

_____

_____

10. Adam represents the age of sin and death, and Christ represents the coming age of life and salvation. The first coming of Christ introduced the age to come. Ever since then the two ages—the age of sin and death and the age of life and salvation—overlap. The age of sin and death will not be completely destroyed until Christ returns.

After reading the explanation of the doctrine of two ages in Arrington's commentary, pages 45-46, 152-54, state the doctrine in your own words.

_____

_____

_____

_____

_____

Pulling It All Together

Core focus and major themes. Look over Romans chapter 5 once again noticing the *Helping Tools* that you have applied to the text. In the text, mark or note major themes in a way that is helpful to you.

In the following table, list at least one core focus for this passage, other major themes you have identified, and what this passage reveals about God's nature.

Core Focus:	
Major Themes:	

Nature of God:	

Summary. Briefly summarize your own interpretation—what you think Paul is saying in the text.

My Interpretation

_____

_____

_____

_____

_____

_____

_____

_____

_____

DEVOTE

Following your exploration of the meaning of the passage, take a few moments to reflect on what you have discerned, and talk to God about it.

- ☐ Invite God to use His Word to change you in any way He desires and to direct you in how you are to apply His Word to your life.

- ☐ Consider writing in a journal or notebook your prayers, inspirations, or any decisions that you make during this time with God.

Pause for Prayer

"Therefore, having been justified by faith, we have peace with God through our Lord Jesus Christ, through whom also we have access by faith into this grace in which we stand, and rejoice in hope of the glory of God." (Romans 5:1-2).

Lord God, You graciously justify us through our faith in Jesus Christ;
You forgive us, cleanse our hearts, minds, and lives, and restore our relationship with You.

I come bowing before You to thank You for your gifts of justification and reconciliation.
Thank You for blessing me and inviting me to stand in Your grace in faith,
so that I can live infused with and rejoicing in the hope of Your glory,
through the grace of my Lord Jesus Christ and the power of the Holy Spirit!

For Reflection & Prayer

☐ In Romans 5:3-5, Paul talks about perseverance in trials that bring about character and hope. Are you going through any sort of difficulty now which requires perseverance and patience? In your circumstance, are you able to see any ways that this difficult time might be developing your character? God wants to help you through your troubles and to use them for good in your life. Consider talking to Him about this situation or challenge, including discussing any frustrations and questions that you might have.

☐ Earlier you were asked to consider the blessings of the gift of justification in your own life—peace, grace, hope, and love. Are there any of these areas that you would like to experience more of? As you talk to God about it, listen for His response within your heart—maybe one or two of these that really stands out to you? Do any ideas come to you regarding how you might go about nurturing and growing these blessings in your life?

☐ In looking back over your notes in this lesson, is there anything else you would like to talk to God about?

☐ At the close of this time of reflection and prayer, consider sitting a few moments in silence with God, being grateful that through His wonderful gift of justification, you are reconciled with Him, and are invited to come any time you want and sit in His holy presence—free and totally forgiven.

DISCIPLE

Consider how you might apply to your daily life what you have been learning and experiencing with God during your study of this passage of Scripture.

Living and Sharing Your Faith

"And not only that, but we also glory in tribulations, knowing that tribulation produces perseverance; and perseverance, character; and character, hope. Now hope does not disappoint, because the love of God has been poured out in our hearts by the Holy Spirit who was given to us." (Romans 5:3-5).

☐ What truths in Romans 5:1-21 have impacted you most? How have they affected the way you think or live?

☐ If you are experiencing some difficulty at this time, what is one action you might take in this circumstance that will help you persevere and place your trust in the hope that God wants to give you?

☐ In the ways that you usually share your faith with others (maybe through your daily routines, conversations, or acts of kindness), how might you communicate the blessings of God's justification—that God loves us all, and through Jesus Christ, offers forgiveness, pardon, and life to anyone who comes to Him?

☐ Are there any commitments that you feel God is leading you to make at this time?

☐   Is there any specific action you would like to take in response to what you have learned during your time in God's Word this week? Ask the Holy Spirit to help you, and take one small step in the direction that you feel Him leading you.

A Closing Prayer

Key Verse:

"For if by the one man's offense death reigned through the one, much more those who receive abundance of grace and of the gift of righteousness will reign in life through the One, Jesus Christ" *(Romans 5:17).* Thank You, Father, You have blessed us!

Jesus, through this lesson this week, I have learned that all of humanity shares in Adam's failures, a path which ultimately leads to death. But You in Your grace, have provided a way back to life. You sacrificed so that we might receive pardon and be declared righteous. Through Your loving act, we can enjoy a guiltless, holy, peaceful status and life with our Heavenly Father.

I welcome You and Your love into my heart.

I invite Your abundant grace and holiness to rule in all of my life.

Open my heart to receive all that You have for me today.

LESSON SEVEN

Romans

CHAPTERS 6:1-23

FREEDOM FROM THE SLAVERY OF SIN

LESSON SEVEN

ROMANS 6:1-23

FREEDOM FROM THE SLAVERY OF SIN

Key Verse

But thanks be to God that, though you used to be slaves to sin, you have come to obey from your heart the pattern of teaching that has now claimed your allegiance. You have been set free from sin and have become slaves to righteousness (Romans 6:17-18, NIV).

Introduction

In Romans 5:1-11, Paul has discussed the blessings of justification by faith. Now in chapters 6–8, he describes at length what is known as the doctrine of sanctification. Being sanctified is to be in a right relationship with God, which requires:

☐ freedom from the slavery of sin through a decisive break with sin (chapter 6),

☐ freedom from the struggle of the rules and regulations of the law (chapter 7), and

☐ ultimately and finally, freedom from the power of death (chapter 8).

In short, sanctification is living as God's children, in the power of the Holy Spirit with hope, being free from the dominion of sin, law, and death.

The word "sanctification" (literally, "holiness") appears only twice in Romans (6:19, 22), and the word "sanctified" only once (15:16). Sanctification emphasizes that it is imperative for Christians to live in a holy manner by obeying the gospel message (6:17). The crucial importance of a holy lifestyle is indicated by the length of Paul's discussion of the doctrine. After Paul focuses on sanctification in Romans chapters 6–8, he will return to the very practical aspects of living the Christian life and the everyday demands of the gospel in Romans 12:1 – 15:13.

New life through the death and resurrection of Christ. At the beginning of chapter 6, Paul returns to the imaginary opponent. As you begin to look at this passage, once again mark the diatribe questions like you have done for previous chapters, placing brackets [ ] around the two questions "spoken" by the opponent (6:1, 15). PLEASE NOTE: The questions in 6:2-3, and 16 are Paul's own questions. Do not bracket those, but place a question mark (?) over each of them like you have been doing to indicate Paul's own rhetorical questions.

Here at the beginning of chapter 6, the opponent is arguing that in view of Paul's teachings about justification by faith, the more one sins the more opportunity God has of being forgiving: "What shall we say then? Shall we continue in sin that sin may abound?" (6:1). Paul's answer is, "Certainly not!" (6:2). God's forgiving grace does not encourage Christians to go on sinning. God's will is not that sin be increased, but that sin cease. Christians are called to a new and holy life. The argument that they should continue to sin is nonsense.

At conversion, the Christian experiences death to the old life of sin and resurrection to a new life of obedience. Paul illustrates the difference between the old life and the new life in Christ by referring to baptism (6:3-11).The immersing of the believer in water is like burial in death and coming out of it to a new life. Through faith, the believer participates in the death and resurrection of Christ, being united with Him in death and raised with Him in newness of life. Because Christ would not compromise with sin, sin killed Him, but God raised Him from the dead. Christ died on behalf of our sin, and the believer who has been united by faith to the crucified, risen Savior, has died to sin. As a person becomes a believer, there is a sharp break with sin similar to a person who dies and breaks with physical life. The old man ("old self," NIV) with its evil thoughts, words, and deeds is crucified (6:6). The believer is a new person, a completely changed person. It makes no sense for a Christian to go on sinning.

Freedom from sin's reign through life lived in God's grace. Paul realizes that a person is not brought to full maturity and made perfect by a single religious experience. So he exhorts his readers to live daily in a way that pleases God (6:12-14). The Roman Christians had been freed from the dominion of sin by faith in Christ, and now, they had the responsibility to live the Christian life. Each day, Christians are to give themselves afresh to God and not to allow their members (parts of their body, "any part of yourself," NIV) to serve sin (6:13). This is possible because the relationship of the believer with God is not governed by the rules and regulations of the Mosaic law, but by the power of God's grace. The believer lives under grace, and grace means freedom from the dominion of the oppressive power of sin.

Moving on, Paul uses an illustration from the institution of slavery (6:15-23). In his time, slavery was widespread in the Roman world. Some of the recipients of his letter were probably slaves or had been slaves. For Paul, all people are slaves—either slaves of sin or slaves of living in accordance with God's Word (6:16). In verse 15, the imaginary opponent argues that since Christians are no longer under law, they can sin as much as they want and still remain right with God. Refuting this view, Paul insists that though Christians are not under law—not expected to keep the rules of the Mosaic law for salvation—this does not mean that obedience to the moral demands of the gospel have no place in the Christian life. Faith and obedience go together. In Romans 1:5, Paul speaks of obedience to the faith, which means a believing submission to Christ. Our whole life is determined by one of two masters: Christ or sin. The issue of whether Christians can go on sinning is settled by Paul. No one can serve Christ and sin at the same time (Luke 16:13). Turning from sin and obedience—to Christ has a fundamental place in a life of grace and faith.

Your Exploration of the Text

Pause for Prayer

"For if we have been united with him [Christ] in a death like his, we will certainly also be united with him in a resurrection like his. For we know that our old self was crucified with him so that the body ruled by sin might be done away with, that we should no longer be slaves to sin" (Romans 6:5-6, NIV).

Lord Jesus, You died for us.

We are united with You both in Your death and in Your resurrection.

Our old selves and our slavery to sin has died, so that we can have a new life

and live as disciples of You, Lord!

Lord Jesus, as I study God's Word, help me understand on a deep level what it means to die daily to any darkness that would try to entice me, and to live fully, in unity with You.

THE TEXT

Romans 5:1-21

[1] What shall we say then? Shall we continue in sin that grace may abound? [2] Certainly not! How shall we who died to sin live any longer in it? [3] Or do you not know that as many of us as were baptized into Christ Jesus were baptized into His death? [4] Therefore we were buried with Him through baptism into death, that just as Christ was raised from the dead by the glory of the Father, even so we also should walk in newness of life.

[5] For if we have been united together in the likeness of His death, certainly we also shall be in the likeness of His resurrection, [6] knowing this, that our old man was crucified with Him, that the body

of sin might be done away with, that we should no longer be slaves of sin. [7] For he who has died has been freed from sin. [8] Now if we died with Christ, we believe that we shall also live with Him, [9] knowing that Christ, having been raised from the dead, dies no more. Death no longer has dominion over Him. [10] For the death that He died, He died to sin once for all; but the life that He lives, He lives to God. [11] Likewise you also, reckon yourselves to be dead indeed to sin, but alive to God in Christ Jesus our Lord.

12 Therefore do not let sin reign in your mortal body, that you should obey it in its lusts. 13 And do not present your members as instruments of unrighteousness to sin, but present yourselves to God as being alive from the dead, and your members as instruments of righteousness to God. 14 For sin shall not have dominion over you, for you are not under law but under grace.

15 What then? Shall we sin because we are not under law but under grace? Certainly not! [16] Do you

not know that to whom you present yourselves slaves to obey, you are that one's slaves whom you

obey, whether of sin leading to death, or of obedience leading to righteousness? [17] But God be thanked

that though you were slaves of sin, yet you obeyed from the heart that form of doctrine to which you

were delivered. [18] And having been set free from sin, you became slaves of righteousness. [19] I speak

in human terms because of the weakness of your flesh. For just as you presented your members as

slaves of uncleanness, and of lawlessness leading to more lawlessness, so now present your members

as slaves of righteousness for holiness.

[20] For when you were slaves of sin, you were free in regard to righteousness. [21] What fruit did you have

then in the things of which you are now ashamed? For the end of those things is death. [22] But now having been set free from sin, and having become slaves of God, you have your fruit to holiness, and

the end, everlasting life. [23] For the wages of sin is death, but the gift of God is eternal life in Christ

Jesus our Lord.

DISCOVER

Keeping in mind the prayer you have just prayed, begin your exploration of Romans chapter 6, observing the text and discovering the facts.

Observing the Text

Helping Questions. Read carefully Romans chapter 6. As you are moving through your reading of the biblical text, create some *Helping Questions* to help you discover the text.

My Helping Questions and Answers:

_____

_____

_____

_____

_____

_____

_____

_____

Observations. Briefly summarize your discoveries, what you have observed so far by using *Helping Questions*.

My Findings:

_____

_____

_____

_____

_____

_____

_____

_____

DISCERN

Now that you have observed the text and discovered some facts, it is time to take a closer look, to explore the meaning of what Paul is communicating in this section of his letter to the Romans.

Marking the Text

Helping Tools. Go through the passage once again applying *Helping Tools*, using TOOLS that you have already used and creating new ones as needed.

Key concepts:

■ Concepts mentioned in this passage for which you have created *Helping Tools* in previous lessons
■ God/People
■ Earthly human condition—*flesh*
■ Old life/New life
■ Baptism imagery: Dead to sin → resurrection → alive to God
■ Slave to sin → freedom → slave to God
■ Under law/Under grace
■ Righteousness of people:
  • Holiness of heart and life—*instruments of righteousness, slaves of righteousness for holiness, fruit to holiness* (6:13, 16-20, 22)
  • Unrighteousness, unholiness in heart and life—*instruments of unrighteousness, slaves of uncleanness* (6:13, 19)
	■ Miscellaneous:
	  • Diatribe:
	    [Jewish opponents' questions] (6:1, 15a-b)
	    [Paul's answers] (6:2-14, 15c-23)
	  • Paul's rhetorical questions (*TIP: They are included in his answers in the diatribe.)
	  • Numbers or amounts
	  • Indications of time
	  • Comparisons, contrasts, repetitions, or progressions and sequences
	  • One or more focus verses
	■ Any other concepts you want to mark

Interpreting the Meaning

Following are questions to help you gain more understanding of the text.

1. Previously in chapter 3, Paul did not complete his response to the question from the imaginary opponent, "If sin gives God a chance to forgive sin, why not increase sinning so that God can be even more gracious" (3:7-8)? Perhaps later on at the end of chapter 5, as Paul was writing the statement, "But where sin abounded, grace abounded much more" (5:20), he realized that the matter had not been settled, so now in chapter 6, he gives a fuller response, indicating that sin should have no place at all in the Christian life.

   Explain what you think the basis is for Paul's answer (6:2-14) to the imaginary opponent's question in verse 1, "Shall we continue in sin that grace may abound?"

   _____

   _____

   _____

   _____

   _____

   _____

   _____

   _____

2. The term sanctification has the broad meaning of holiness and indicates freedom over the power of sin. With a strong emphasis on the gospel of grace and forgiveness of sin, there is always the danger of believers in the 21st century assuming that they no longer have to take sin seriously. Even though the old self with its evil thoughts, words, and deeds has been put to death (6:6), Christians are still tempted and have desires to sin.

   What can Christians do to ensure greater maturity and conformity to Christ in thought and deed?

   _____

   _____

   _____

   _____

   _____

   _____

   _____

   _____

   _____

3. When a person becomes a believer, there is a spiritual break with the old life, as sharp as the break that occurs in when a person dies a physical death, leaving behind their life on this earth. Water baptism does not save a person, but it is an act of obedience to the Lord and pictures the decisive move from the old way of life to another.

How would you explain the significance of baptism to a person who has not yet received the forgiveness that God offers—using baptism as a picture of the experience of forgiveness?

_____

_____

_____

_____

_____

_____

_____

4. Jesus Christ lived a sinless life, but Paul says, "He died to sin…" (6:10). This statement does not mean that Christ died to sin as believers have. Christ's death did not release Him from a love of sin or from the power of sin. Verse 10 becomes clearer if we understand that Christ took the consequences of our sins on Himself and bore them for us.

Do you remember when you first realized that Christ died in your stead? How do you feel about His sacrifice? Describe your thoughts, feelings, and response.

_____

_____

_____

_____

_____

_____

_____

5. In 6:11, Paul introduces the idea of being in Christ, one of the most important themes in Paul's writings. That is, when we come to faith in Christ, we enter into union and fellowship with Him; and only in Christ are we holy, separated from all that is vile, evil, and unclean.

   Why is it such a privilege and honor to be in union with Christ and to be called the holy people of God?

   _____

   _____

   _____

   _____

   _____

   _____

   _____

   _____

   _____

6. Paul realizes that under the gospel, God's people are released from having to live by the rules of the Mosaic law—that in their new life in Christ, they are to live free, no longer ruled by the power of sin (6:2, 7, 11). Even so, Paul recognizes that a single religious experience (conversion) does

not make believers perfect, and that in order to grow and live a life that reflects the character of Christ, daily attention to holiness is needed. So in 6:12-14, Paul shifts from the topic of union with Christ to the topic of the demands of everyday living.

In Paul's exhortations here, he may be taking into consideration that his readers' lifestyles possibly have been falling short of the ideal for a new life in Christ, or at least that there is some danger of them falling back into their old life, by giving into sinful desires and practices. Paul encourages them to present themselves and their lives as instruments to God for His holy use (6:13). To do otherwise is for them to risk forfeiting their salvation. Indeed, to know Christ personally is not only a spiritual experience, it is an ongoing way to live one's life.

Explain why Christianity is not just a one-time spiritual experience, but a way of life.

_____

_____

_____

_____

_____

_____

7. In 6:1, the imaginary opponent's question, "Shall we continue in sin that grace may abound?" could be translated: "If God takes unrestrained pleasure in forgiving, He will forgive anyway, so

why not go on sinning?" The way Paul answers this question reminds us of Jesus' teaching about sin, recorded in Luke 16:13.

According to Jesus, why is it that no person can serve God and sin?

_____

_____

_____

_____

_____

_____

_____

8. In the first century world, slave owners dominated the lives of their slaves; they had the power of life and death. For Paul, life is determined by one of two masters—Christ or sin. Sin pays its slaves with death. Christ gives those who serve Him eternal life. In the text, underline 6:23 and memorize this wonderful reminder of the gift of life we have through our Lord Jesus Christ!

Pulling It All Together

Core focus and major themes. Look over Romans chapter 6 once again noticing the *Helping Tools* that you have applied to the text. In the text, mark or note major themes in a way that is helpful to you.

In the following table, list at least one core focus for this passage, other major themes you have identified, and what this passage reveals about God's nature.

Core Focus:	
Major Themes:	

Nature of God:	

Summary. Briefly summarize your own interpretation—what you think Paul is saying in the text.

My Interpretation

_____

_____

_____

_____

_____

_____

_____

_____

_____

_____

_____

_____

DEVOTE

Following your exploration of the meaning of the passage, take a few moments to reflect on what you have discerned, and talk to God about it.

- ☐ Invite God to use His Word to change you in any way He desires and to direct you in how you are to apply His Word to your life.

- ☐ Consider writing in a journal or notebook your prayers, inspirations, or any decisions that you make during this time with God.

Pause for Prayer

"But now that you have been set free from sin and have become slaves of God, the benefit you reap leads to holiness, and the result is eternal life" (Romans 6:22, NIV).

Holy Father, You are our Deliverer. You set us free from captivity.

Today, I want to present myself to You as your servant and slave. Help me to live a life focused on and permeated with Your goodness and holiness. I want to serve You forever, stepping into each day and each moment confident, through the hope that Your glorious promise of eternal life gives me.

For Reflection & Prayer

☐ In Romans 6, Paul talks about dying to sin and being alive to God, and says that we were once slaves to sin and now we're slaves to God. Are there any areas in your life where you might be living as a slave to sin, even though Christ has set you free to live abundantly as a servant of God?

- Talk to Jesus about those areas, and allow Him to forgive you and to give you strength and courage to die to (to turn and walk away from) any darkness in your thoughts or actions that might be holding you captive.

- Listen for any wisdom or guidance that the Holy Spirit might be giving you to help you live fully in your position of freedom in Christ.

☐ Paul tells us that as followers of Christ, we have been united with Christ in His death and resurrection. How does that make you feel? Does it give you hope?

☐ In looking back over your notes in this lesson, is there anything else you would like to talk to God about?

DISCIPLE

Consider how you might apply to your daily life what you have been learning and experiencing with God during your study of this passage of Scripture.

Living and Sharing Your Faith

"...Offer yourselves to God as those who have been brought from death to life; and offer every part of yourself to him as an instrument of righteousness" (Romans 6:13, NIV).

☐ What truths in Romans 6:1-23 have impacted you most? How have they affected the way you think or live?

☐ Thinking about your conversation that you had with God during your DEVOTION time about dying to sin and being alive to God, what do you think it would look if you were to live fully free from sin? How might your life change? How might your relationships change?

☐ To help us live free from the slavery of sin, God provides us ongoing help in many forms. In thinking about your own personal struggles and weaknesses, consider if there might be a particular action or spiritual practice that might be helpful to you.

• Maybe you want to consider attending a group fellowship or study that deals with the challenges you are facing?

- Maybe there is a trusted person with whom you might talk or pray—someone who is known for his or her gifts of wisdom and encouragement, or a mature Christian who has dealt with similar life experiences, or maybe someone who has special expertise in addressing the questions you have?

  As ideas come to mind, write them in your prayer journal and ask the Holy Spirit to lead you in the direction you need to go. (For ideas for spiritual practices, see Arrington's commentary: "Appendix G: Practices That Nurture Our Faith and Holy Living," p. 430-433.)

- ☐ Are there any commitments that you feel God is leading you to make at this time?

- ☐ Is there any specific action you would like to take in response to what you have learned during your time in God's Word this week? Ask the Holy Spirit to help you, and take one small step in the direction that you feel Him leading you.

A Closing Prayer

Key Verse:

"But thanks be to God that, though you used to be slaves to sin, you have come to obey from your heart the pattern of teaching that has now claimed your allegiance. You have been set free from sin and have become slaves to righteousness" (Romans 6:17-18, NIV).

Father, we were all slaves of sin, but You have lifted us out of our slavery and set us free. You have changed our hearts and have empowered us to become servants of Your holiness.

In the days ahead, please show me how I, as your servant, might reflect in my daily life this holiness that You have placed in me;

Show me how I might love others and share Your message of freedom with them— the same Good News that has set me free.

ENLIVEN
ENCOUNTERING GOD
through
HIS WORD

LESSON EIGHT

Romans

CHAPTERS 7:1-25

FREEDOM FROM THE LAW

LESSON EIGHT

ROMANS 7:1-25

FREEDOM FROM THE LAW

Key Verse

But now, by dying to what once bound us, we have been released from the law so that we serve in the new way of the Spirit, and not in the old way of the written code (Romans 7:6, NIV).

Introduction

Christians understand the importance of being free from sin, but why should we be free from the law? When Paul speaks of the law, he primarily has in mind the rules and regulations of the Hebrew people that are recorded in their Scriptures (Exodus through Deuteronomy), which include commandments as well as prohibitions of moral law.

The role of the law. The law is God's gift, which forbids sin and demands obedience. Obedience of the gospel and obedience of faith are diffcrent from obedience in a legalistic sense of keeping the law for salvation. Christians are to have nothing to do with legalism and efforts of trying to earn salvation. Instead, we are to depend on Christ for salvation, not on ourselves and keeping of the law. Salvation is by faith in Christ and results in a life change as definite as when a person dies.

The moral law does remain as a guide for us in living the Christian life. The law is holy, righteous, and good (7:12), but it is inadequate to secure salvation for us and to enable us to live a sanctified, holy life. So in Romans 7, Paul deals with the relationship between the law and sanctification, living the Christian life. The Christian no longer lives under the authority of the law, but under the authority of Christ. Jesus is our Lord, and we owe our obedience to Him.

Death to legalism through the death of Christ. Paul has emphasized that Christians have died to sin (Romans 6:2-11), but they also are dead to the law. Having made a complete break with legalism, they now rely only on Christ for salvation. For example, Paul appeals to the rules of marriage and remarriage to illustrate that death cancels contracts. When a woman's husband dies, she is no longer obligated to her marriage vows (7:1-6). Death cancels the marriage contract and she is free. Likewise, only spiritual death can free us from condemnation of the law (the consequences of guilt from not keeping all of God's commandments). Our relationship with the law of legalism has been dissolved because we have been united with Christ in His death. Never can our relationship with God be based on legalism, but on our fellowship with Christ whom God raised from the dead. Our old relationship to the law has been replaced by our new relationship with Christ.

Reliance on the grace of God through Christ, and the power of the Holy Spirit.

In Romans 7:7-25, the first person pronoun (I, my, me) is used almost fifty times. This has prompted scholars to debate whether this section is autobiographical, referring only to Paul. If we assume it refers only to Paul, then the question is—Is Paul describing himself before Christ met him on the road to Damascus or as the Christian who is writing the letter of Romans to believers in Rome? Chapter 7 certainly sounds autobiographical, but sometimes the pronoun "I" includes Paul and others as well (Rom. 3:7; 1 Cor. 13:1-3). If we understand that the pronoun "I" is broader than Paul, there still remains the question of whether he is describing himself before conversion or after conversion. There is room for difference of opinion.

The law can continue to be an issue in the Christian life, and believers can continue to struggle with temptation and still be victorious. But we must rely on the grace of God through Christ and the guidance and the power of the Holy Spirit in order to live victoriously. Romans teaches that humans before and after conversion cannot serve God through human strength. Throughout life, human effort to keep God's law results in failure.

Misuse of the Law. But now, Paul goes on to indicate the effect that sin can have on the law. Though the law is holy, righteous, and good, sin can take something as good as the law, a gift from God's own hand, and make it serve the ends of evil (7:11-12). Observing the ceremonies and rules of the Old Testament may appear to be good religion, but one may keep the law for the wrong reasons. Many first century Jews did not keep the law out of love and gratitude for God, but for the purpose of winning rewards for themselves.

Keeping rules and regulations for the wrong reasons leads to the bondage of legalism and despair (7:23-24). Sin will corrupt the best of human efforts. God's purpose for the law is to define right and wrong, not to deliver us from sin. The law is weak and cannot help us deal with the sin problem. Sin will take God's holy law and use it to bring about evil. Our only hope is absolute dependence on Christ. The practice of religion, whether it is Judaism or Christianity or any other religion, will save no one. Christ and Christ alone is the answer as Paul's thanksgiving suggests: "I thank God—through Jesus Christ our Lord!" (7:25).

Your Exploration of the Text

Pause for Prayer

"What shall we say, then? Is the law sinful? Certainly not! Nevertheless, I would not have known what sin was had it not been for the law." (Romans 7:7, NIV).

Thank You, God, for Your law that shows us when we are in error and need to turn to You for forgiveness, guidance, and strength. Your commandments create healthy boundaries around our lives that help protect our souls.

During my study of Your Word, please teach me how to relate to Your sacred law in ways that are true to the new path of grace that You offer me through your Son Jesus Christ.

THE TEXT

Romans 7:1-25

[1]Or do you not know, brethren (for I speak to those who know the law), that the law has dominion over a man as long as he lives? [2]For the woman who has a husband is bound by the law to her husband as long as he lives. But if the husband dies, she is released from the law of her husband. [3]So then if, while her husband lives, she marries another man, she will be called an adulteress; but if her husband dies, she is free from that law, so that she is no adulteress, though she has married another man. [4]Therefore, my brethren, you also have become dead to the law through the body of Christ, that you may be married to another—to Him who was raised from the dead, that we should bear fruit to God.

[5] For when we were in the flesh, the sinful passions which were aroused by the law were at work in our members to bear fruit to death. [6] But now we have been delivered from the law, having died to what we were held by, so that we should serve in the newness of the Spirit and not in the oldness of the letter.

[7] What shall we say then? Is the law sin? Certainly not! On the contrary, I would not have known sin except through the law. For I would not have known covetousness unless the law had said, "You shall not covet." [8] But sin, taking opportunity by the commandment, produced in me all manner of evil desire. For apart from the law sin was dead. [9] I was alive once without the law, but when the commandment came, sin revived and I died. [10] And the commandment, which was to bring life, I found to bring death. [11] For sin, taking occasion by the commandment, deceived me, and by it killed

me. [12] Therefore the law is holy, and the commandment holy and just and good.

[13] Has then what is good become death to me? Certainly not! But sin, that it might appear sin, was producing death in me through what is good, so that sin through the commandment might become exceedingly sinful. [14] For we know that the law is spiritual, but I am carnal, sold under sin. [15] For what I am doing, I do not understand. For what I will to do, that I do not practice; but what I hate, that I do.

[16] If, then, I do what I will not to do, I agree with the law that it is good. [17] But now, it is no longer I who do it, but sin that dwells in me. [18] For I know that in me (that is, in my flesh) nothing good dwells; for to will is present with me, but how to perform what is good I do not find. [19] For the good that I will to do, I do not do; but the evil I will not to do, that I practice. [20] Now if I do what I will not to do, it is no longer I who do it, but sin that dwells in me.

[21] I find then a law, that evil is present with me, the one who wills to do good. [22] For I delight in the law of God according to the inward man. [23] But I see another law in my members, warring against the law of my mind, and bringing me into captivity to the law of sin which is in my members. [24] O wretched man that I am! Who will deliver me from this body of death? [25] I thank God—through Jesus Christ our Lord!

So then, with the mind I myself serve the law of God, but with the flesh the law of sin.

DISCOVER

Keeping in mind the prayer you have just prayed, begin your exploration of Romans chapter 7, observing the text and discovering the facts.

Observing the Text

Helping Questions. Read carefully Romans chapter 7. As you are moving through your reading of the biblical text, create some *Helping Questions* to help you discover the text.

My Helping Questions and Answers:

_____

_____

_____

_____

_____

_____

_____

_____

_____

Observations. Briefly summarize your discoveries, what you have observed so far by using *Helping Questions*.

My Findings:

_____

_____

_____

_____

_____

_____

_____

_____

_____

_____

_____

_____

_____

DISCERN

Now that you have observed the text and discovered some facts, it is time to take a closer look, to explore the meaning of what Paul is communicating in this section of his letter to the Romans.

Marking the Text

Helping Tools. Go through the passage once again applying *Helping Tools*, using TOOLS that you have already used and creating new ones as needed.

Key concepts:

- Concepts mentioned in this passage for which you have created *Helping Tools* in previous lessons
- God/People
- Death—Marriage image
- Sin
- The law—*law, letter, commandment*
- Righteousness of God's law:
  - Rightness and holiness of God's law (holy in a moral sense, being right from God)—*the law is holy, the commandment holy* (7:12)

- Slavery—*captivity, dominion, bound*
  Freedom—*free, released, delivered*
- Holy, Just, Good
- Miscellaneous:
  - Numbers or amounts
  - Indications of time
  - Rhetorical questions
  - Comparisons, contrasts, repetitions, or progressions and sequences
  - One or more focus verses
- Any other concepts you want to mark

Interpreting the Meaning

Following are questions to help you gain more understanding of the text.

1. Paul's use of the marriage/remarriage illustration to explain the concepts of death and the law does not indicate that the law died, but that the believer has died to the law and left it behind.

   How does union with Christ through faith set the believer free from the law?

_____

_____

_____

_____

What distinction should be made between keeping the law for salvation (legalism) and observing the Ten Commandments as a guide to the Christian life?

_____

_____

_____

_____

_____

2. In 7:4, Paul speaks about serving God, stating, "we should bear fruit to God."

List five ways we can be productive (fruitful) in our service to God.

_____

_____

_____

_____

_____

_____

_____

_____

3. In 7:6, Paul says that we are to serve God in the newness of the Spirit ("in the new way of the Spirit," NIV). Explain how this relates to freedom from the law and new life in Christ.

_____

_____

_____

_____

_____

_____

4. Paul and many others have realized that they could not measure up to the demands of the law in their own strength. What is the strength and the weakness of the law, and what has been your experience in trying to keep the law as an unbeliever and believer?

_____

_____

_____

_____

_____

_____

_____

_____

_____

_____

5. As you are aware, some people think that Paul in 7:21-24 is describing the "good" person who struggles with the law before he or she is saved; others think that the person is saved and struggles daily to live the Christian life. Which do you think is appropriate and why?

_____

_____

_____

_____

_____

6. Paul said that the believer dies to the law (7:4, 7). This could lead to the question: Is the law sinful? The answer is not provided until verse 12, where the law is described as holy, just, and good. Beginning with verses 7-11, Paul illustrates the problem with the law. He remembers the time when he thought he was sinless, but the true significance of the tenth commandment, "You shall not covet," dawned on him (Rom. 7:7; Ex. 20:17; Deut. 5:21). Sin had been latent, but it sprang to life. Sin used the tenth commandment which is holy, just, and good to provoke Paul to covet and do the forbidden.

Perhaps you can relate having a similar experience when you were a child? You may have been innocently doing wrong. Then when you learned from an adult that your action was wrong and told not to do it, the new restriction placed on you seemed to fuel your desire to do the forbidden. (Maybe you are struggling with something now in your life. If so, consider pausing here and talking to God about it. Receive His grace, and ask Him for wisdom and strength.)

_____

_____

_____

_____

_____

_____

7. Paul affirms that the law is good, but that sin uses the law, as good as it is, to lead persons into bondage and despair. Give some instances where sin has taken good things (loyalty, generosity, holiness, or other examples) as avenues to achieve its evil ends.

_____

_____

_____

_____

_____

_____

8. Individuals cannot save themselves, but this does not release them from personal responsibility. Why is this true?

_____

_____

_____

_____

_____

_____

_____

9. The struggle between the human will and human actions continues. In Romans 7, Paul describes an inner, spiritual struggle.

Do you think that such a struggle is characteristic of the Christian life? Explain.

_____

_____

_____

_____

_____

_____

Summary. Briefly summarize your own interpretation—what you think Paul is saying in the text.

My Interpretation

DEVOTE

Following your exploration of the meaning of the passage, take a few moments to reflect on what you have discerned, and talk to God about it.

- ☐ Invite God to use His Word to change you in any way He desires and to direct you in how you are to apply His Word to your life.

☐ Consider writing in a journal or notebook your prayers, inspirations, or any decisions that you make during this time with God.

Pause for Prayer

"So I find this law at work: Although I want to do good, evil is right there with me. For in my inner being I delight in God's law; but I see another law at work in me, waging war against the law of my mind and making me a prisoner of the law of sin at work within me. What a wretched man I am! Who will rescue me from this body that is subject to death? Thanks be to God, who delivers me through Jesus Christ our Lord!" (Romans 7:21-25, NIV).

Heavenly Father, You rescue us from sin, and deliver us from drowning in our failures and guilt, which the law creates in us.

Even though I want to obey You—in my own human power, I lack the self-discipline to overcome my unhealthy passions, desires, and habits. Thank You, God, for providing a way for me to move beyond my struggles to keep Your law, so that I can live in Your freedom.

Thank You for empowering me through Your Holy Spirit to live victoriously in the grace, forgiveness, and love of my Lord Jesus Christ!

For Reflection & Prayer

☐ In this passage of Scripture, Paul indicates the law of God, even though holy, can cause us to stumble if we do not view it properly. How do you feel about Paul's observation that focusing on prohibitions of the law can lead a person to be tempted and to actually sin?

☐ Are there any areas of your life in which you struggle with being legalistic—relying on your own effort to keep God's law, rather than on His grace? Invite Jesus Christ and His love and grace into those areas.

☐ In looking back over your notes in this lesson, is there anything else you would like to talk to God about?

DISCIPLE

Consider how you might apply to your daily life what you have been learning and experiencing with God during your study of this passage of Scripture.

Living and Sharing Your Faith

"So, my brothers and sisters, you also died to the law through the body of Christ, that you might belong to another, to him who was raised from the dead, in order that we might bear fruit for God." *(Romans 7:4, NIV).*

☐ What truths in Romans 7:1-25 have impacted you most? How have they affected the way you think or live?

☐ Earlier in your reflection and prayer time, you were asked look at any tendency you might have toward legalism. Pray and ask the Holy Spirit to help you with any area in which you are prone to be legalistic and to work things out on your own. Ask Him to show you what might help you rely more on His guidance and strength in living a life of faith.

In the spirit of God's grace, consider if there might be a simple spiritual practice that would help you focus less on legalism and self-judgment and live more in Jesus' love and grace. An example of such a practice is: A person who is struggling with jealousy and coveting might begin taking a few moments each day to express gratitude to God for his or her blessings and to pray that others will be blessed, too. Over time, God can use these moments of focusing on Him and His love to transform one's heart, mind, and life in powerful ways.

☐ Are there any commitments that you feel God is leading you to make at this time?

☐ Is there any specific action you would like to take in response to what you have learned during your time in God's Word this week? Ask the Holy Spirit to help you, and take one small step in the direction that you feel Him leading you.

A Closing Prayer

Key Verse:

"But now, by dying to what once bound us, we have been released from the law so that we serve in the new way of the Spirit, and not in the old way of the written code" (Romans 7:6, NIV).

God, thank You for Your law that shows us our need for You.
I come to You today with my desire to serve You and keep Your commandments.

You give me assurance that even though I have failed in my intentions in the past,
You have forgiven me and You still love me deeply.
You kindly set me free from the shame and condemnation of rules and regulations,
and offer me a new and better path—the way of being led by the Holy Spirit.
Thank You for placing Your Spirit in me to love, guide, and empower me.

LESSON NINE

Romans

CHAPTERS 8:1-39

NEW LIFE IN THE HOLY SPIRIT

LESSON NINE

ROMANS 8:1-39

NEW LIFE IN THE HOLY SPIRIT

Key Verse

For those who live according to the flesh set their minds on the things of the flesh, but those who live according to the Spirit, the things of the Spirit (Romans 8:5).

Introduction

In the previous chapters of Romans, Paul has been discussing the new life that comes to those who believe in Christ. He has spoken emphatically about this new life including freedom from sin (Romans 6) and the law (Romans 7), and now he speaks about freedom from death—not necessarily freedom from physical death, but freedom from ultimate, final death.

The Holy Spirit and new life. Through the first seven chapters of Romans, Paul has referred to the Holy Spirit only three times. He speaks in 1:4 of the Spirit of holiness, in 5:5 of the love of God has been poured out in our hearts by the Holy Spirit, and in 7:6 that we should serve in the newness of the Spirit. The new life in the Spirit is the theme of Romans 8. This is the great chapter in Romans on the Holy Spirit. In fact, here Paul tells us more about the boundless possibilities and realities of the Spirit's work in believers than in any other place in his letters. The magnificence of chapter 8 can hardly be overemphasized. It is not surprising that this chapter has been called the Pentecost of Romans. With this strong emphasis on victory through the power and guidance of the Spirit, Paul continues to focus on sanctification, as he has in chapters 6 and 7.

Full salvation. Up to this point, Paul has established that the believer through faith in Christ is treated as righteous by God. The believer is being saved (1 Cor. 1:18), but not fully and finally saved. Full salvation will be experienced at the second coming of Christ. So even though the believer has been delivered from the power and control of sin and from the condemnation of the law, he or she still lives in a fallen world and is confronted by temptation and Satan.

The law of our life—unity with Christ and the power of the Spirit. In Romans 8, Paul expresses the central theme of justification in a new way, using the phrase "in Christ Jesus" (Rom. 8:1). The believer is freed from condemnation (the legal consequences of wrongdoing) because he or she is in union with Christ. In Romans 8:2, we meet two laws: (1) the law (religion) of the Spirit of life, which is made possible by the saving work of Christ Jesus; and (2) the law of sin and death, meaning the way of legalism, which is the unsuccessful human effort to keep the law in order to earn salvation, resulting in death. So "law" here refers to the controlling principle in our lives that determines our behavior.

The person who lives under the rule of Christ is renewed, transformed, and directed by the Holy Spirit. Therefore, the divine way is believing obedience, which can only be achieved by our living through the power of the life-giving Spirit and in fellowship with Christ. What God did through His Son is responsible for the Christian life. God's act of sending His Son into this world did what nothing else could do (Rom. 8:3)—set us free from the powers of sin and death. Christ came into the rough and tumble of human life, and unlike Adam, He overcame every temptation to sin.

The Holy Spirit, a vital member of the Godhead. Paul knows that life dominated by sinful interest and concerns is hostile toward God and cannot please Him. The language of Romans 8:9-11 reminds us of the intimate relationship of the Holy Spirit with the other two persons of the Godhead: God the Father and God the Son. The Spirit is described as the Spirit of God and the Spirit of Christ. Each of the persons are fully God and have an intimate relationship with one another. Our relationship with Christ depends on the Holy Spirit. Without the Holy Spirit's presence in our lives we do not belong to Christ. The Christian life is lived in fellowship with the Father, the Son, and the Holy Spirit.

Living as children of God through the Holy Spirit. The Christian is not to pursue a life determined by sinful ambitions, desires, and passions, but rather a life led by the Spirit (Rom. 8:12-30). As a result of being indwelt, empowered, and directed by the Spirit, believers have holy character as the sons and daughters of God. Spirit-led believers have not received the spirit of bondage again to fear (a spirit of slavery that leads them back into fear), but the Spirit of adoption, enabling them to cry out in prayer, "Abba Father," with the assurance that they are sons and daughters of God (v.

15). The word Abba is Aramaic, the language that the Jews normally used, and is the affectionate term that a Jewish child would use to address his or her father. Jesus used this word when He spoke to God. Paul has used several great grace words in describing salvation: justification, reconciliation, and redemption. Now he adds another—adoption, which makes us aware of our adoption into God's family with all the rights and privileges of being His children. It is a status that comes to us not as a natural right but as a gift from our Heavenly Father.

Freedom for God's creation and the whole natural order. The time is coming when all of nature and the whole natural order will be set free from the curse of Adam's disobedience and fall. Eden, once the perfect world, gave way to much suffering and hardship (Gen. 3:17-18). God's children will be delivered from present suffering and will share in glorious liberty as members of God's family (Rom. 8:18-25). Along with God's delivering His people, He will also restore His creation. In the meantime, endurance is possible for God's people through the help of the Holy Spirit (8:26, 27), for they have the assurance that the divine purpose includes their salvation (8:31-39).

God's promise of salvation—predestination, the called, and the elect. The assurance we have in God's promise of grace and salvation is also discussed in Romans 8:29-30, 33. There has been much debate over the meaning of verses 29, 30, and 33. Some have argued that the term "predestined" indicates a type of double predestination—that some are destined for heaven and others for hell. Predestination and elect are biblical words and in this passage are used somewhat differently than how we would use them today. These words, simply put, mean that God took the initiative to provide salvation for all people; that even before He created the world, God chose (elected), predetermined and planned (predestined) to make provision for salvation (Eph. 1:4; 2 Tim. 1:9; 1 Pet. 1:20).

Throughout human history, God has always been calling people to salvation. Through His self-revelation, He has invited everyone into relationship with Him—revealing Himself through His creation; historical events; His holy written Word; the life, death, and resurrection of His Son Jesus Christ; the voice and fruit of His Holy Spirit; and the gifts of His people. The gospel is a gospel of grace, and it is for everyone. All are invited to accept Christ as their Savior. God has planned the way of salvation, but He allows each person to choose whether or not to accept this gift and to enter into the life of blessing that He offers.

The power of God's love. Paul concludes this part of Romans, Romans 1–8, with a climax to his discussion (8:31-39). The love of God (5:5, 8) is the same as the love of Christ (8:35). God's love stands at the heart of Paul's teaching about justification by faith. There will be persecutions and troubles for believers, but none of these can separate believers from Christ, who is surely Lord as He is love. Christ is more powerful than all adversities, whether earthly or cosmic. Nonetheless, Paul does not say that sin and unbelief cannot separate us from Christ. In fact, writing to the Christians in Rome, he warned them that if they live according to the flesh (human nature) they would die (8:13). Good behavior will not save us, but if we choose to engage in actions contrary to God's ways, we are choosing to distance and separate ourselves from our Savior. This underscores the importance of doing God's will and living a holy life.

Through the power of the Holy Spirit, God gives us the strength to face all our challenges—those brought on by circumstances, people, or powers outside ourselves, as well as any darkness we may experience within ourselves. We can call on the Holy Spirit in all of life's circumstances and in all of our moments of weakness. The Spirit will give us wisdom and strength, so that we can face anything that threatens to interfere in our relationship with God. Guided and empowered by the Holy Spirit who lives in us, nothing can separate us from God's love, which He has revealed to us through our Lord Jesus Christ!

Your Exploration of the Text

Pause for Prayer

"There is therefore now no condemnation to those who are in Christ Jesus, who do not walk according to the flesh, but according to the Spirit" (Romans 8:1).

"But if the Spirit of Him who raised Jesus from the dead dwells in you, He who raised Christ from the dead will also give life to your mortal bodies through His Spirit who dwells in you" (Romans 8:11).

Father, You offer us new life, fellowship with our Lord Jesus Christ,
And You empower us to live this new life through Your Holy Spirit.

In my time with You in this study of Romans chapter 8, please teach me more about
how I can walk with Your Spirit in this new life You have given me.

THE TEXT

Romans 8:1-39

[1]There is therefore now no condemnation to those who are in Christ Jesus, who do not walk according to the flesh, but according to the Spirit. [2]For the law of the Spirit of life in Christ Jesus has made me free from the law of sin and death. [3]For what the law could not do in that it was weak through the flesh, God did by sending His own Son in the likeness of sinful flesh, on account of sin: He condemned sin in the flesh, [4]that the righteous requirement of the law might be fulfilled in us who do not walk according to the flesh but according to the Spirit. [5]For those who live according to the flesh set their minds on the things of the flesh, but those who live according to the Spirit, the things of the

Spirit. [6] For to be carnally minded is death, but to be spiritually minded is life and peace. [7] Because the carnal mind is enmity against God; for it is not subject to the law of God, nor indeed can be. [8] So then, those who are in the flesh cannot please God.

[9] But you are not in the flesh but in the Spirit, if indeed the Spirit of God dwells in you. Now if anyone does not have the Spirit of Christ, he is not His. [10] And if Christ is in you, the body is dead because of sin, but the Spirit is life because of righteousness. [11] But if the Spirit of Him who raised Jesus from the dead dwells in you, He who raised Christ from the dead will also give life to your mortal bodies through His Spirit who dwells in you.

[12] Therefore, brethren, we are debtors—not to the flesh, to live according to the flesh. [13] For if you

live according to the flesh you will die; but if by the Spirit you put to death the deeds of the body,

you will live. [14] For as many as are led by the Spirit of God, these are sons of God. [15] For you did not

receive the spirit of bondage again to fear, but you received the Spirit of adoption by whom we cry

out, "Abba, Father." [16] The Spirit Himself bears witness with our spirit that we are children of God,

[17] and if children, then heirs—heirs of God and joint heirs with Christ, if indeed we suffer with Him,

that we may also be glorified together.

[18] For I consider that the sufferings of this present time are not worthy to be compared with the glory

which shall be revealed in us. [19] For the earnest expectation of the creation eagerly waits for the

revealing of the sons of God. [20] For the creation was subjected to futility, not willingly, but because of

Him who subjected it in hope; [21] because the creation itself also will be delivered from the bondage of corruption into the glorious liberty of the children of God. [22] For we know that the whole creation

groans and labors with birth pangs together until now. [23] Not only that, but we also who have the

firstfruits of the Spirit, even we ourselves groan within ourselves, eagerly waiting for the adoption,

the redemption of our body. [24] For we were saved in this hope, but hope that is seen is not hope; for

why does one still hope for what he sees? [25] But if we hope for what we do not see, we eagerly wait

for it with perseverance.

[26] Likewise the Spirit also helps in our weaknesses. For we do not know what we should pray for as

we ought, but the Spirit Himself makes intercession for us with groanings which cannot be uttered. [27]

Now He who searches the hearts knows what the mind of the Spirit is, because He makes intercession

for the saints according to the will of God.

[28] And we know that all things work together for good to those who love God, to those who are the called according to His purpose. [29] For whom He foreknew, He also predestined to be conformed to the image of His Son, that He might be the firstborn among many brethren. [30] Moreover whom He predestined, these He also called; whom He called, these He also justified; and whom He justified, these He also glorified.

[31] What then shall we say to these things? If God is for us, who can be against us? [32] He who did not spare His own Son, but delivered Him up for us all, how shall He not with Him also freely give us all things? [33] Who shall bring a charge against God's elect? It is God who justifies. [34] Who is he who condemns? It is Christ who died, and furthermore is also risen, who is even at the right hand of God, who also makes intercession for us. [35] Who shall separate us from the love of Christ? Shall tribulation,

or distress, or persecution, or famine, or nakedness, or peril, or sword? [36] As it is written:

"For Your sake we are killed all day long;

We are accounted as sheep for the slaughter."

[37] Yet in all these things we are more than conquerors through Him who loved us. [38] For I am persuaded that neither death nor life, nor angels nor principalities nor powers, nor things present nor things to come, [39] nor height nor depth, nor any other created thing, shall be able to separate us from the love of God which is in Christ Jesus our Lord.

DISCOVER

Keeping in mind the prayer you have just prayed, begin your exploration of Romans chapter 8, observing the text and discovering the facts.

Observing the Text

Helping Questions. Read carefully Romans chapter 8. As you are moving through your reading of the biblical text, create some *Helping Questions* to help you discover the text.

My Helping Questions and Answers:

_____

_____

_____

_____

_____

_____

_____

_____

_____

Observations. Briefly summarize your discoveries, what you have observed so far by using *Helping Questions*.

My Findings:

_____

_____

_____

_____

_____

_____

_____

_____

_____

_____

_____

_____

DISCERN

Now that you have observed the text and discovered some facts, it is time to take a closer look, to explore the meaning of what Paul is communicating in this section of his letter to the Romans.

Marking the Text

Helping Tools. Go through the passage once again applying *Helping Tools*, using TOOLS that you have already used and creating new ones as needed.

Key concepts:

■ Concepts mentioned in this passage for which you have created *Helping Tools* in previous lessons	■ Righteousness of God:
	• Jesus Christ's holiness and atoning act of justification—*righteousness* (8:10)
■ God/Holy Spirit *TIP: Observe how frequently Paul mentions the Holy Spirit.	■ Righteousness of people:
	• Holiness of heart and life—*righteous requirement of the law* (8:4)
■ Other supernatural beings	■ Called/Foreknowledge/Predestination/Elect
■ People	■ Justification
■ Death / Life	■ Adversity and hardships—*tribulation*
■ *Law*—controlling principle in life that determines behavior (8:2, 7)	■ Love
	■ Miscellaneous:
■ *Law*—God's commandments recorded in the Old Testament (8:3-4)	• Numbers or amounts
	• Indications of time
■ Slavery—*bondage* Freedom—*delivered, liberty, redemption*	• Rhetorical questions
	• Comparisons, contrasts, repetitions, or progressions and sequences
■ Prayer—*pray, intercession*	• One or more focus verses
■ Family—*sons, adoption, children, heirs*	■ Any other concepts you want to mark

Interpreting the Meaning

Following are questions to help you gain more understanding of the text.

1. All of God's Word is precious to us. Some parts of the Scriptures are very special. To Pentecostals, Romans 8 is one of those passages because its emphasis is that the Holy Spirit leads us daily and gives us victory over temptations and the flesh (human nature). The dark cloud that seems to hang over parts of chapter 7 has been removed, and the light of the gospel is shining brightly in chapter 8. Having read chapter 8, describe your impressions of it. Perhaps it raised particular questions in your mind, or a few verses have grabbed your attention.

_____

_____

_____

_____

_____

_____

_____

_____

2. Paul has talked about believers being in a right relationship with God through faith; and that as a result, we have peace with God (Rom. 5:1). Underscoring the stunning implications of the gospel, he adds, "There is therefore now no condemnation to those who are in Christ Jesus, who do not walk according to the flesh, but according to the Spirit" (Rom. 8:1). Even though God has erased our condemnation and guilt, some believers think that this is too good to be true and continue to struggle with guilt about the past.

Have you had this struggle or have known someone who has? How would you help a person who is a Christian who does not have the assurance that the sin and guilt of the past have been blotted out?

_____

_____

_____

_____

_____

_____

3. A frequent theme in Paul's letters is the contrast between flesh and Spirit. His use of the term flesh does not refer to the body itself, but to human nature that inhabits the body and can control the body. This flesh (nature) is an enemy of the Holy Spirit, prompting one to pursue sinful interests that go against the will of God. In Galatians 5:19-21, Paul says that the works of the flesh include hatred, contentions, jealousies, outbursts of wrath, selfish ambitions, and the like.

    In light of this, how do you understand the law of the Spirit of life versus the law of sin and death (8:2)?

_____

_____

_____

_____

_____

_____

_____

_____

_____

4. The purpose of God's sending His Son was not only for justification, but for sanctification, so that the demands of the moral law may be fulfilled in us as we walk in the Spirit (Rom. 8:4). Remember that Paul does not offer us a definition of the Holy Trinity in Romans, but an experience in which we live to God, Christ, and the Holy Spirit.

    What kind of commitment do you think that requires? Does it require our mind, body, emotions, and will (8:5-8)? Discuss your thoughts and ideas for living in this way.

_____

_____

_____

_____

_____

_____

_____

_____

What will the different outcomes be between: (1) living the way human nature wants us to live, and (2) living a Spirit-filled life in accordance with Acts chapter 2?

_____

_____

_____

_____

_____

_____

_____

5. Notice three ideas that Paul mentions in Romans 8:5-17: (1) You have not the Spirit (vs. 5-8), (2) The Spirit dwells in you (vs. 9-11), and (3) The Spirit has you (vs. 12-17).

Discuss each of these ideas. Especially give attention to the second and the third conditions, noting a factor that Paul indicates is key to these types of relationships with the Holy Spirit. Also give attention to the fact that we do not need to be defeated as believers, for we have no obligation to live according to the flesh (fallen human nature).

_____

_____

_____

_____

_____

_____

_____

_____

6. In Romans 8:15, Paul uses the word "adoption" to express the joy of our new relationship through Christ. In the NIV, this concept is translated as "your adoption to sonship" (8:15). In the surrounding verses (14 and 16), Paul uses the phrases "sons of God" and "children of God." These terms all indicate that our gift of salvation includes a new relationship with God that is similar to the relationship that an adopted child has with an adoptive parent. This is a new status through which God gives sinners the rights and privileges of being His daughters and sons. These rights are not natural rights, but are rights our gracious God bestows on all believers and prepares them to live a new life in His family.

List what human adoption does for a child and what God's adoption does for sinners.

Human adoption _____

_____

_____

_____

_____

_____

God's adoption _____

_____

_____

_____

_____

_____

_____

_____

_____

7. Verses 19-23 of Romans 8 tell us that the whole natural order suffered from Adam's disobedience and fall. As all humankind fell with Adam, so the perfect world came under suffering and trouble. But in the end time, the natural order will share in redemption and restoration.

Can you describe evidence that the natural order is groaning and travailing under the oppressive burden of sin, discord, and decay, and why Paul ties together the transformation of the whole world and the final salvation of believers?

_____

_____

_____

_____

_____

_____

_____

8. Paul, turning aside from his discussion of the hope of final salvation for both believers and creation, turns to speak of the important ministry of the Holy Spirit in prayer (Rom. 8:26-27). He describes the Holy Spirit as praying for us with groanings which cannot be uttered. At times believers may be overwhelmed with problems or circumstances. They may be weak and not know how to pray. Paul himself prayed for God to remove his own thorn, but this was not God's will. The Spirit comes to help us in our present weakness and prays for us using groans and sighs that cannot be uttered in human words. Many Pentecostal believers have testified that at times when they were unable to express their needs and burdens, the Holy Spirit prayed through them in a prayer language unknown to them. This prayer language is known as glossolalia or speaking in tongues.

If you have had such an experience, describe it. If not, perhaps there is someone you know who has. That person may be able to describe it to you, and help you understand the experience. What assurance do we have that God understands such prayer?

_____

_____

_____

_____

_____

_____

_____

_____

_____

_____

9. There has been a lot of theological controversy surrounding Romans 8:29-30. Simply put, Paul's intent in these verses is to communicate that salvation comes from God. The word translated "purpose" means that God has a plan for salvation (8:28). The word "predestined" indicates that God took the initiative in providing salvation for all people, and He decided the way of salvation before He created this world. The focus of verses 29 and 30 is on those who have chosen to trust in Christ. God has predestined (determined in advance) that those of us who are led by the Spirit are to be conformed to the image of His Son (8:29).

Later in verse 33, Paul's use of the phrase "God's elect" continues this train of thought, referring to the ones who have accepted God's call to salvation. God elects to offer salvation to all, and through His predestined plan, He allows each individual the freedom to choose whether or not he or she enters the way of salvation. Relationship with God is a mutual, personal relationship that includes the freedom of choice and is open to all.

In view of Paul's teachings on predestination and human free will, how would you respond to a person who believes that the ultimate destiny of each person is determined before birth? (See Arrington's commentary, pages 224-230.)

_____

_____

_____

_____

_____

_____

10. Romans 8:31-39 brings us to the end of a major part of this letter. Believers today need to face the reality of suffering, pain, and spiritual warfare. Paul did not teach that all things would be easy for us, but he does assure us, "If God is for us, who can [successfully] be against us?" (8:31). If God were against us, we would have no hope. Even though Paul sees the Christian life as a challenge and a fight against darkness, he gives us the assurance that the fury of Satan and unbelievers cannot prevail as long as we are directed and empowered by the Spirit.

Why should Paul's thoughts recorded here and in previous chapters of Romans give us comfort and confidence that God is able to sustain us in trials and troubles?

_____

_____

_____

_____

_____

_____

_____

_____

11. In verse 35, Paul gives a list of troubles that will not separate us from Christ's love. By this time, Paul has experienced all of these troubles, except the sword (death). Many of these troubles were afflicted on the early Christians, as well as on Christians today in countries where they are persecuted.

Have you experienced or witnessed any of the troubles on Paul's list? If so, what was your experience of the love of Christ during that time? Today when you think of that situation, how do you perceive His presence then?

_____

_____

_____

_____

_____

_____

_____

_____

_____

12. The love of Christ should not be seen as different from God's love. In verses 38-39, the Apostle answers the question: "Who shall separate us from the love of Christ?" (v. 35). He enumerates powers that may threaten believers, but that cannot prevail. List them and explain the nature of each of the powers.

_____

_____

_____

_____

_____

_____

_____

_____

13. On the basis of Romans 8:4-14, list the characteristics of believers who walk according to the Spirit.

_____

_____

_____

_____

_____

_____

_____

14. On the basis of Romans 8:2-29 list what the Holy Spirit does for believers.

_____

_____

_____

_____

_____

_____

_____

_____

_____

Pulling It All Together

Core focus and major themes. Look over Romans chapter 8 once again noticing the *Helping Tools* that you have applied to the text. In the text, mark or note major themes in a way that is helpful to you.

In the following table, list at least one core focus for this passage, other major themes you have identified, and what this passage reveals about God's nature.

Core Focus:	
Major Themes:	

Nature of God:	

Summary. Briefly summarize your own interpretation—what you think Paul is saying in the text.

My Interpretation

_____

_____

_____

_____

_____

_____

DEVOTE

Following your exploration of the meaning of the passage, take a few moments to reflect on what you have discerned, and talk to God about it.

- ☐ Invite God to use His Word to change you in any way He desires and to direct you in how you are to apply His Word to your life.

- ☐ Consider writing in a journal or notebook your prayers, inspirations, or any decisions that you make during this time with God.

Pause for Prayer

"For those who are led by the Spirit of God are the children of God"… "The Spirit himself testifies with our spirit that we are God's children" (Romans 8:14, 16, NIV).

God, You are our loving Father. Through Jesus Christ, You have placed Your Spirit in us and call us Your children.

Help me in this time with You to feel Your love and acceptance. Help me to see myself as a real member of Your family.

For Reflection & Prayer

☐ The Holy Spirit is with you in all of life, and He helps you in your prayers. Invite the Spirit into this time of reflection and prayer.

☐ In your life, how do you feel when instead of setting your mind on things of this world, you set your mind on things of the Spirit?

☐ Meditate on the fruit of the Spirit that Paul lists in Galatians 5:22-23: "But the fruit of the Spirit is love, joy, peace, longsuffering [patience, perseverance, constancy], kindness, goodness, faithfulness, gentleness, self-control. Against such there is no law."

• Pause a moment, and thank God that through the Lord Jesus Christ, you have been given the Holy Spirit and these wonderful fruits.

• At this point in your life, which of these fruit of the Spirit do you need more of? Ask the Holy Spirit to help you in this area.

• When you think about living your life very present with the Holy Spirit, experiencing all the fruit He offers you, do you feel differently about yourself? About God? About your life and your purpose on this earth? Take a moment and talk to God about that.

☐   As a follower of Christ, you are a child of God, and an heir of His kingdom. How does knowing that you are a vital part of God's family make you feel? Is there anything about being a member of His family you would like to discuss with God, or maybe thank Him for?

☐   In looking back over your notes in this lesson, is there anything else you would like to talk to God about?

DISCIPLE

Consider how you might apply to your daily life what you have been learning and experiencing with God during your study of this passage of Scripture.

Living and Sharing Your Faith

"And we know that in all things God works for the good of those who love him, who have been called according to his purpose." (Romans 8:28, NIV).

"...If God is for us, who can be against us? He who did not spare his own Son, but gave him up for us all—how will he not also, along with him, graciously give us all things? (Romans 8:31-32, NIV).

☐   What truths in Romans 8:1-39 have impacted you most? How have they affected the way you think or live?

☐ Earlier during your reflection and prayer time, you considered what life fully lived in the Holy Spirit feels like. Now take a few moments to consider how living fully in the Spirit might actually change your life. What things would you think about? How would it affect your priorities and daily routines? How would it affect your relationships? Tell the Holy Spirit your desires for a life focused on His ways and living more completely in His spiritual fruit.

☐ Be encouraged, as you walk in the Spirit, God will give you strength to do whatever He calls you to do. God will work in every situation to bring about good, and no person, force, or difficult circumstance can separate you from God's love! Are there any areas in which you desire extra power, wisdom, and grace today, so that you can live a life that is more fully focused on things of the Spirit?

☐ As you are considering walking in new life in the Spirit, are there any commitments that you feel God is leading you to make at this time?

☐ Is there any specific action you would like to take in response to what you have learned during your time in God's Word this week? Ask the Holy Spirit to help you, and take one small step in the direction that you feel Him leading you.

A Closing Prayer

Key Verse:

"For those who live according to the flesh set their minds on the things of the flesh, but those who live according to the Spirit, the things of the Spirit" (Romans 8:5).

God, You created us and all the world around us.

You save us through Your Son Jesus Christ, who walks with us through all of life.

You place in us Your Holy Spirit to guide and give us strength in the journey.

As part of Your holy family, we can always be assured and feel comforted that You will take the details of our lives and work them together to bring about good.

With You on my side, I don't have to be afraid of anything!

You will give me what I need;

You have even given Your Son Jesus to purchase my freedom and to give me life.

I can live victoriously and abundantly in the power of your Spirit!

Thanks be to God!

Lesson Ten

Romans

Chapters 1-8

Wrap-Up

LESSON TEN

ROMANS: CHAPTERS 1-8

WRAP-UP

Key Verse

And we know that all things work together for good to those who love God, to those who are the called according to His purpose...What then shall we say to these things? If God is for us, who can be against us? He who did not spare His own Son, but delivered Him up for us all, how shall He not with Him also freely give us all things? (Romans 8:28, 31-32).

Introduction

Romans is a message about life in Jesus Christ. Think about it, in about 57 or 58 A.D. Paul wrote this letter on a back street in the city of Corinth. The fame of his letter has far outlived the Apostle Paul. Its acclaim does not surprise us because it is part of the inspired Word of God and has helped Christians for generations to understand the glorious truths of the gospel. We do not know if Paul ever wondered how he would be remembered. If he did, we can only imagine what he would think today of the long-term outcome of his work. His thirteen letters (by the count of many) have been read now for about 2,000 years in languages throughout the world.

Remembering the importance of Romans. Once again, let us recall why the content of Paul's letter to the Romans has been so influential and significant to the church. Paul's letter communicates the life-transforming message of the gospel and deals with the essential questions about salvation and living the Christian life. His letter brings to us a deeper understanding of our own salvation and a greater sense of our connection with one another as believers in Christ. It feeds our hearts with stimulating truths and our minds with fresh channels of thoughts. The letter confronts the human mind with the truths of God, and casts every person on the mercy of the Divine Redeemer. Of the 66 books of the Bible, none of them challenges us like the book of Romans. This book strips away complacency and pride, exposing the futility of our trying to save ourselves. Not only, however, does this letter raise questions about our relationship with God (justification by faith), but it also raises questions about practical matters such as walking by faith, relationships inside and outside the church, ministry to the church and the world, weaknesses and failures of believers, the importance of spiritual gifts, and believing and practicing sound doctrine.

Nowhere in the Bible can we find a more complete statement of Christian doctrine than in Romans. In this exposition Paul uses the great words and doctrinal concepts:

☐ repentance, sin, judgment, wrath, law,

- ☐ justification, redemption, propitiation, atonement, reconciliation, adoption,

- ☐ righteousness, grace, gospel, faith, imputation, sanctification,

- ☐ death, resurrection, revelation,

- ☐ the presence of the Holy Spirit, gifts of the Spirit,

- ☐ foreknowledge, elect, predestination, calling,

- ☐ glorification, and purpose.

Indeed, Paul's letter to the Romans is a valuable key to understanding the entire Bible, both the Old Testament and the New Testament, and is a profound defense of the gospel message.

The Apostle Paul. Paul's vocation was not writing, but preaching. His message is steeped in what God did in Christ, which is the high point of his letter to the Romans. In fact, Paul, as one of the world's greatest apostles, is also one of the world's greatest missionaries and writers. It can accurately be said that the day of this greatest letter, Romans, is not over. In fact, it will have a vast influence until Christ returns.

Good News about salvation. At this point, you have studied chapters 1–8 of Paul's letter to the Romans in which He has set forth the doctrine of salvation:

- ☐ He has stressed the world's need of salvation (1:18 – 3:20).

- ☐ He has summarized the spiritual condition of humankind in the words: "all have sinned and fall short of the glory of God" (3:23).

☐   He has emphasized the meaning and importance of justification by faith (1:16, 17; 4:1 – 5:11).

☐   Here and there, he has referred to his own people, the Jews, and has mentioned that they have the advantage of having the Scriptures of the Old Testament (3:1-2; compare 9:3-5). He has pointed out that despite the importance of the Jewish people's advantages and that the gospel was offered to the Jew first (1:16), the Jews and Gentiles were equal before God, in that spiritually they both stood in need of God's grace and salvation (2:1 – 3:21).

☐   The death of Christ on the cross is personal: Christ died for us, the ungodly (5:6). As the ultimate act of love, Christ died for all of us, in order to set us free from the slavery of sin. He died even for the enemies of God.

Good News about freedom in Christ. The gospel saves us and liberates us from the worst part of ourselves so that we can thrive in Christian community and please God. Living in freedom in Christ means living in grace, free from the burdens that our inability to perfectly follow rules and regulations create for us. Living a virtuous life without Christ will not save us, but such a life is the necessary means for spiritual growth, remaining in close relationship with God, and experiencing the blessings of salvation. The truth is that we cannot live the Christian life without divine grace. As we have noted, living in the freedom of God's grace is especially Paul's concern in Romans chapters 6–8. Chapter 6 teaches freedom from the power of sin; chapter 7 freedom from the condemnation of the law; and chapter 8 freedom from ultimate death. As children of God, the Holy Spirit sanctifies us so that we are no longer under the dominion of sin, law, and death.

Good News about holiness of life. The gospel is good news about our being counted as holy by God and about living a righteous, holy life that is pleasing to God. There are two parts to sanctification: God's action and the believer's response. Both parts are placed side by side in Leviticus 20: "I am the Lord who sanctifies you" (v. 8); "Consecrate yourselves, therefore, for I am the Lord your God" (v. 7). Like the Old Testament, Paul sees sanctification as being rooted in God's work. We are to live and walk accordingly. So the sanctified life is the result of what God has done and continues to do through the Holy Spirit and our willingness to dedicate ourselves to serving and pleasing God. Through God's Holy Spirit, whom He has placed in our hearts, we have the peace and power to live moment to moment dedicated to the holiness of our Lord Jesus Christ!

Good News in suffering. God allows His people to suffer, but He Himself suffered in the person of His Son, so that we would have life and hope (8:32). Even though we share in the suffering of Christ in this life, through our faith in Him, we can take comfort and place our hope in God's promises. He will give us wisdom and strength through our difficulties. He will bring about good in all our life circumstances. And one day He will honor us, and we will get to enjoy life with Him, in His presence and glory, forever.

Conclusion. So far, you have studied many of the great truths about the gospel in Romans chapter 1–8. We hope that this has been a meaningful adventure for you and that you have developed a desire for more. Perhaps in the future, you will find occasions to come back to your study of Romans, to look over the notes you have made in your Discovery Guide and prayer journal, and to revisit what you have learned and experienced during this time with God and His Word. There is always something new to learn from this magnificent letter.

There is more to come, for the whole of Romans is a power-packed letter! In fact, there is not a more complete statement of gospel truths in the Bible than in Paul's letter to the Romans. In the sequel to our study of Romans 1–8, we will explore Romans chapters 9–16.

Before we conclude our study of Romans 1–8, we want to take some time to take note of what we have learned, to thank God for the insights we have gained and the blessings we have experienced, and to consider where God is calling us to go from here.

Your Exploration of the Text

Once again, let's take a look at Romans 1–8, to remember, to be thankful, and to ask for God guidance in the days ahead.

Pause for Prayer

"Therefore, I urge you, brothers and sisters, in view of God's mercy, to offer your bodies as a living sacrifice, holy and pleasing to God—this is your true and proper worship" (Romans 12:1, NIV).

I come to You, Father, and offer myself to You.
I worship You—through my thanks, my study of Your written Word, and through my actions.

Speak to me once again through Your Word, so that I can know You better and walk with You in all I say and do.

DISCOVER

Romans 1–8 as a whole. Now that you have journeyed through Romans chapters 1–8, discovering and discerning the facts and meanings of this wonderful text of the Bible, it is good to take some time to go back through the passage and experience the entire text in a fresh, new way—as a whole.

☐ In your *Discovery Guide*, reread chapters 1–8 of the text of Paul's letter to the Christians in Rome. As you read through this NKJV text, glance at the *Helping Tools* you created. The tools you have applied to the text will help bring the meaning to life for you again.

What was different about this experience from your previous readings of this passage of Scripture? Did you have any new insights, thoughts, or feelings about the passage? Note any thoughts here or in your prayer journal.

_____

_____

_____

_____

_____

_____

_____ - _____

Do any new questions come to mind? Note them here, and consider exploring them later in your personal study or during group discussion time.

_____

_____

_____

_____

_____

☐ Now branch out a bit and experience another version of the biblical text. Reread Romans chapters 1–8 in the NIV or some other version of your choice. Notice how the newness of expression of a different version of the Bible can help you discover new insights and expand your experience with the text.

In this reading, in order to experience more fully the text of Romans as a real conversational letter, you may want to read aloud to yourself or listen to a recording. You can find recordings of the Bible online at: https://www.biblegateway.com/resources/audio/, http://www.biblestudytools.com/audio-bible/, http://www.bible.is/download/audio, or possibly borrow an audio Bible from your local public or church library.

After you have read or listened to Romans 1–8 in a different version, please answer these questions: What was different about this experience from your previous readings of this passage of Scripture? If you read the text aloud or listened to a recorded reading, how did hearing the Word of God impact you? Do you have any new insights, thoughts, or feelings about Romans chapters 1–8?

_____

_____

_____

_____

_____

_____

_____

_____

DISCERN

Pause for Prayer

"Do not conform to the pattern of this world, but be transformed by the renewing of your mind. Then you will be able to test and approve what God's will is—his good, pleasing and perfect will" (Romans 12:2, NIV).

Father, during our inductive study of Your Word, You have been transforming us and renewing our minds. Thank You!

As I begin my review of the wonderful truths and insights You have shown me during my time in Your Word, please continue to change and transform me. Help me to understand Your ways, to be the person You created me to be, and to live according to Your good, pleasing, and perfect will.

Pulling It All Together

Themes & Insights. Now that you have had a fresh experience with God's Word through reading Romans 1–8 as a whole, pause and take some time to think about what you have learned over the course of this study. Go back through each lesson in your *Discovery Guide* and look at the tables where you recorded your insights about core focuses, major themes, and the nature of God.

☐ **Core Focus**. In the space provided below, copy in brief form each core focus that you discovered during this inductive study, so that you have a combined list of the primary topics that Paul has addressed in chapter 1–8 of his letter.

☐ **Life impact**. Going back through your *Discovery Guide* again, look over the major themes that you listed in each lesson. Are there any of these themes that have really impacted you—your relationship with God, how you think, feel, or live? Note those below.

☐ **Nature of God**. Now look back over the notes you made about the nature of God in each lesson. During this study, did you discover anything new about God? Has your new knowledge about God affected your relationship with Him? Record any new insights that you want to be sure to remember.

☐ **Questions to explore**. Looking at what you have written below, do any new questions come to mind? Maybe you have questions you want to raise in the group discussion time during the final session of this study, or questions you want to explore with God in prayer, or maybe questions that you would like to discuss with a mentor or pastor. Note those below.

_____

_____

_____

_____

_____

_____

_____

_____

_____

_____

_____

_____

_____

_____

_____

Core Focus	
LESSON TWO (1:1-17)	
LESSON THREE (1:18-2:29)	
LESSON FOUR (3:1-31)	

Core Focus	
LESSON FIVE (4:1-25)	
LESSON SIX (5:1-21)	
LESSON SEVEN (6:1-23)	

Core Focus	
LESSON EIGHT (7:1-25)	
LESSON NINE (8:1-39)	

Core Focus

LIFE IMPACT:	

Core Focus	
Nature of God:	
QUESTIONS I HAVE	

DEVOTE

Following your review of the wisdom and insights God has given you during this study, it is good to make some space to talk to Him about what you have learned, and to invite Him to speak to you and to work His transforming love and power in your life.

Pause for Prayer

One way to give God opportunity to work in your life is to meditate on and pray about a passage of Scripture from God's Word. To do so:

1. Review through your *Discovery Guide*, looking over the *Key Verses* for each lesson and other verses listed in the *Pause for Prayer* sections. Choose a verse for this time of prayer and conversation with God. Maybe you have a favorite verse; or maybe you feel prompted by the Holy Spirit to look more closely at a particular verse.

2. Write your verse on a piece of paper or index card. (Writing the verse will help you think more closely about it, and will also help you focus during your time of prayer.)

3. Now read the verse that you have selected a few times. It can be helpful to read the verse aloud, and in each reading emphasize different words or phrases in order to help bring the meaning to life.

4. After you have read through the verse, talk to God about the truths you are noticing in the passage. Tell Him what is on your heart. You may want to thank Him, tell Him what you are thinking and feeling, or ask Him some questions.

5. As you complete this time of prayer, pause a few moment in silence to be with God and to open your heart to anything His Spirit wants to say to you.

6. Note in your prayer journal anything you wish to remember from this special time with God.

For Reflection & Prayer

Continuing in a prayerful attitude, we want to consider some of the wonderful words and phrases Paul has used in Romans. Below are some of those that you have encountered during this study. Throughout his letter, Paul has used words and phrases that are rich in meaning. They carry the power to enlighten, to encourage, and to inspire one to pursue a relationship with God.

Take a few moments to read through the words and phrases listed below and think about them. You may find that as you look at them, they help you recall experiences that you have had with God's Word during this study. Consider the following as you read:

☐ How do you feel as you read through these words and phrases? Are there any particular ones that touch your heart?

☐ What is your experience with God as you are reading through this list? Do you sense God speaking to you through any of them?

☐ Talk to God, and note in your prayer journal any thoughts you want to remember.

1:1-17

Opening of Paul's Letter

Paul, a bondservant of Jesus Christ
- called
- to be an apostle
- separated to the gospel of God

- to all in Rome who are loved by God and called to be his holy people (NIV)
- impart to you some spiritual gift to make you strong—that is, that you and I may be mutually encouraged by each other's faith (NIV)

- not ashamed of the gospel
- it is the power of God to salvation for every one who believes
- in it the righteousness of God is revealed from faith to faith
- the just shall live by faith

1:18-2:29

THE WORLD'S NEED OF SALVATION

- suppress the truth in unrighteousness
- professing to be wise
- became fools
- treasuring up for yourself wrath in the day of wrath

- righteous judgment of God
- eternal life to those who by patient continuance in doing good seek for glory, honor, and immortality
- to those who are self-seeking and do not obey the truth, but obey unrighteousness—indignation and wrath, tribulation, and anguish

---

- you, therefore, who teach another, do you not teach yourself?
- you who make your boast in the law, do you dishonor God through breaking the law?
- circumcision is that of the heart, in the Spirit

3:1-31

ALL PEOPLE EQUAL IN THEIR NEED OF SALVATION

- all under sin

- whatever the law says, it says to those who are under the law, so that every mouth may be silenced and the whole world held accountable to God (NIV)
- through the law we become conscious of our sin (NIV)

- now the righteousness of God apart from the law is revealed
- being justified freely by His grace through the redemption that is in Christ Jesus
- whom God set forth as a propitiation [sacrifice of atonement] by His blood, through faith

- By what law? Of works? No, but by the law of faith
- Do we then make void the law through faith? Certainly not!
- we establish the law

4:1-25

SALVATION THROUGH FAITH

- to the one who does not work but trusts God who justifies the ungodly, their faith is credited as righteousness (NIV)

Words of David:

- Blessed are those whose lawless deeds are forgiven, and whose sins are covered

- Blessed is the man to whom the Lord shall not impute sin [*shall not count his sin against him*]

- It was not through the law that Abraham and his offspring received the promise that he would be heir of the world, but through the righteousness that comes by faith (NIV)

- against all hope, Abraham in hope believed (NIV)

- The words "it was credited to him" were written not for him [Abraham] alone, but also for us, to whom God will credit righteousness—for us who believe in him who raised Jesus our Lord from the dead (NIV)

5:1-21

THE BLESSINGS OF JUSTIFICATION

- justified by faith

- peace with God through our Lord Jesus Christ

- glory in tribulations $\rightarrow$ perseverance $\rightarrow$ character $\rightarrow$ hope

- the love of God has been poured out in our hearts by the Holy Spirit

---

- Christ died for the ungodly

- Christ died for us

- free gift

- by the grace of one Man, Jesus Christ

- abundance of grace

- gift of righteousness

- free gift came to all men [people]

- resulting in justification of life

- eternal life

6:1-23

FREEDOM FROM THE SLAVERY OF SIN

- died to sin

- baptized into Christ Jesus

- baptized into His death

- walk in newness of life

- old man was crucified with Him [Christ]

- freed from sin

- alive to God in Christ Jesus our Lord

- not under law but under grace

- set free from sin

- slaves of righteousness

- having been set free from sin, and having become slaves of God

  → have your fruit to holiness,

  → and the end, everlasting life

- wages of sin is death

- the gift of God is eternal life in Christ Jesus our Lord

7:1-25

FREEDOM FROM THE LAW

- become dead to the law through the body of Christ →

- that you may be married to another—to Him who was raised from the dead →

- bear fruit to God

- serve in the newness of the Spirit and not in the oldness of the letter

---

- sinful passions which were aroused by the law were at work in our members to bear fruit to death

- the law is holy, and the commandment holy and just and good

- I would not have known what sin was had it not been for the law (NIV)

- with the mind I myself serve the law of God, but with the flesh the law of sin

- Who will deliver me from this body of death? I thank God—through Jesus Christ our Lord!

8:1-39

New Life in the Holy Spirit

- no condemnation to those who are in Christ Jesus

- who do not walk according to the flesh, but according to the Spirit

- to be spiritually minded is life and peace

- though your body is subject to death because of sin, the Spirit gives life because of righteousness (NIV)

- for those who are led by the Spirit of God are the children of God (NIV)

- the Spirit Himself bears witness with our spirit that we are children of God

- if children, then heirs—heirs of God and joint heirs with Christ

---

- the sufferings of this present time are not worthy to be compared with the glory which shall be revealed in us

- we hope for what we do not see

- we eagerly wait for it with perseverance

- the Spirit also helps in our weaknesses

- the Spirit Himself makes intercession for us

- all things work together for good to those who love God

- if God is for us, who can be against us?

- in all these things we are more than conquerors through Him who loved us

- [nothing] shall be able to separate us from the love of God which is in Christ Jesus our Lord

DISCIPLE

Now that you have spent some special time with God contemplating the treasures in His Word, and giving thanks for the blessings that you have enjoyed during this inductive study of Romans, prepare to consider how you might apply your new insights to your life.

Living and Sharing Your Faith

"Therefore, having been justified by faith, we have peace with God through our Lord Jesus Christ, through whom also we have access by faith into this grace in which we stand, and rejoice in hope of the glory of God...Now hope does not disappoint, because the love of God has been poured out in our hearts by the Holy Spirit who was given to us" (Romans 5:1-2, 5).

- ☐ Think again, during your inductive study of Romans 1–8, what truths of Romans have impacted you most? How have they affected the way you think or live?

- ☐ How might you and your church reflect these truths in the life of your church, your community, and in the world?

- ☐ As you think about your time in study and fellowship with the other students who have been on this journey with you, is there anything you would like to say to them? Do you feel the Holy Spirit directing you to partner with any of them in ministry? Talk to God about that.

☐ Are there any commitments that you feel God is leading you to make at this time?

☐ Is there any action you would like to take in response to what you have been learning and experiencing during your time in God's Word during this inductive study? Ask the Holy Spirit to help you, and begin to plan how you will proceed in the days ahead.

Looking Ahead

You have now completed your inductive study of Romans 1–8! You have learned about the heart of God for you—the love, freedom, and transformation that He offers you through His Son Jesus Christ. You have learned about His Holy Spirit whom He has placed in you to guide you, strengthen you, and give you peace and hope.

As you have studied chapters 1–8, no doubt at times, there have been occasions when you were digging into the text of Romans that a verse or passage grabbed or jumped out at you. We might call this experience a moment of truth in which the Holy Spirit illuminates the biblical text and enables you to make sense of a particular passage and apply it to your life. This kind of interpretative interaction with God's Word and the Holy Spirit is deeply satisfying and helps us to understand that what has been given by the Spirit should be interpreted by the aid of the Spirit. The more we know about God's Word, the more we know about God, and through the Holy Spirit's illumination, we are able to hear God's voice and draw close to Him in our hearts and lives.

This has been an incredible journey through this very important letter included in God's Holy Word. We pray that you have experienced God's love and will go out from here to love and serve our Lord Jesus Christ, in the power and blessing of the Holy Spirit.

Let's take a few moments to get a glimpse of some of the grand themes coming up in the next part of Romans (chapters 9–16). In this portion of Paul's letter, we will learn more about God's work of salvation in the world and how we can go about living the transformed life that God has given us. Here is a quick overview of the topics we will cover:

- ☐ Paul's love for his people, Israel

- ☐ Had God been fair to Israel and faithful to His promises to them?

- ☐ More Gentiles had accepted Christ. Had God's plan for Israel failed?

- ☐ Why did God use Isaac and Jacob to advance His plan of salvation, rather than Ishmael and Esau?

- ☐ The importance of apostolic, Spirit-empowered preaching

- ☐ The remnant of Israel and the Christian church today

- ☐ True worship in changed lives

- ☐ Spiritual gifts in the body of Christ, the church

- ☐ Christians and civil government

- ☐ Love fulfills the law

☐ End time urgency

☐ Vegetarians and meat-eaters—relationships between the stronger and weaker in faith

☐ Relationships and fellowship in the church today

☐ Paul's plans for travel and Spirit-empowered ministry

We hope you will be able to join with us to explore these interesting and transformational topics during the second half of our study of Paul's letter!

A Closing Prayer of Blessing

May you go forward in blessing and fellowship with God our Father and Creator, our Lord and Savior Jesus Christ, and the Holy Spirit of peace and power!

"Yet in all these things we are more than conquerors through Him who loved us. For I am persuaded that neither death nor life, nor angels nor principalities nor powers, nor things present nor things to come, nor height nor depth, nor any other created thing, shall be able to separate us from the love of God which is in Christ Jesus our Lord." (Romans 8:37-39)

Thanks be to God!

APPENDIX

Romans

CHAPTERS 1-8

GOD'S PLAN OF SALVATION

APPENDIX

GOD'S PLAN OF SALVATION

SALVATION

The total work of God to bring humankind from a state of sin

to a state of eternal life through Jesus Christ

=

God

God / Godhead / Holy Trinity—The spiritual entity, ruler of the universe, and social being comprised of three persons: Father, Son, and Holy Spirit, who is righteous (right, holy), all-powerful, all-knowing, infinite, eternal, and unchangeable in being, wisdom, and glory.

God's Self-Revelation • Propitiation (atonement) • Calling

God, The Father and Creator—*Reveals Himself through His creation and natural order.* God, the originator and maker of everything, reveals Himself through the world He has created: through the whole world, everything in it, and the organization of its components and processes, all of which have been created and set in motion by His command. He sent His Son Jesus to the earth to reveal Himself to all of creation and to redeem and set right the damage that sin has caused the whole world.

Jesus Christ, The Son of God—*Has revealed God through His life on earth, and His death, and resurrection.* Jesus came to earth in human form to live among us, in order to teach us about God, demonstrate God's love for us, and pay the penalty for the sins of humanity through His suffering and death (His propitiation and atoning sacrifice for us). God has revealed His own power over sin and death and His life-giving nature through the resurrection of Jesus. Jesus Christ now is with the Father, and reveals His love to us and is present with and in us through the power of the Holy Spirit.

The Holy Spirit—*Reveals God by calling us, enlightening us, and living in us.* The Holy Spirit is the third person of the Holy Trinity and the Spirit of God, who calls people to eternal life in Christ in various ways. He speaks through God's written Word and responds directly to one's prayer and heart desire to know God. The Holy Spirit often calls and speaks to us through people who preach, teach, or demonstrate the love of God in their lives. In calling, the Holy Spirit speaks to people's consciences to convict them of sin and their need for God, and He illuminates their minds to be open and receptive to the Good News of Christ and to receiving His love. When someone comes to Jesus Christ and commits his or her life to Him, the Holy Spirit bestows spiritual fruit and gifts, and gives guidance, power, and peace for living the Christian life.

Scripture / God's Word—*The holy writings of the Bible that reveal God to us and teach us about Him and His involvement with humanity.* The Scripture is the primary means by which God speaks to us personally through the power of His Holy Spirit.

The Gospel—*God's revelation of Good News about His plan for salvation,* through which He invites each of us to an eternal life with Him, by way of His redemptive activity through Jesus Christ.

Our Belief • Repentance • Faith

Belief—Belief in God, belief in Christ

Repentance—Remorse for sin (actions and attitudes contrary to the will of God), turning from sin and asking for forgiveness

Faith—Trust and reliance on God

Grace • Redemption • Forgiveness • Justification

Grace—Unearned favor and blessings from God

Redemption—Deliverance from some form of bondage secured by the payment of a ransom

Forgiveness—God's act of pardon, acquitting a person of sins, declaring that person not guilty

Justification—God's act of declaring a person to be righteous (in right standing with Him)

Adoption • Reconciliation

Adoption—An act of grace by God in which He chooses to place a person as His son or daughter, and bestow on that believer the status and blessings of membership in His family

Reconciliation—Restoration of personal relationship between God and a person

Righteous, Sanctified Position

Righteousness—A gift from God of being in right standing with Him through His love, grace, and forgiveness

Sanctification—Being in a position of holiness and purity through relationship with God; positional sanctification

Righteous, Sanctified Life

Life of Righteousness—A holy life, which is a life lived in faith and trust in God, governed by God's love

Sanctification—The ongoing practice and experience of living in relationship with God, submitting to His ways, and allowing Him to transform a person; practical sanctification

Hope • Eternal Life • Glory

Hope—Confidence in God that He will always do what He has promised

Eternal Life—The gift from God of living in His love and presence forever

Glory—At Christ's second coming, the resurrected state of the believer, a new life and body on the order of Christ's glorified body

About the Author

A resident of Cleveland, Dr. Arrington is professor emeritus of New Testament Greek and Exegesis at the Pentecostal Theological Seminary. A scholar of the New Testament and the Greek language, he served for 21 years as a PTS faculty member as well as 17 years with Lee University. While at Lee, he was chairman of the Bible and Theology Department, and honored with the Excellence in Teaching Award.

Dr. Arrington was ordained in the Church of God in 1968. In addition to preaching in numerous churches around the world, he served as assistant pastor of the East Atlanta Church of God and as pastor of the Tower Grove Church of God in St. Louis.

Dr. Arrington has authored numerous books and contributed to many other publications. His latest book, *The Greatest Letter Ever Written: A Study of Romans*, is available at Pathway Press.

Dr. Arrington's academic degrees include a Doctor of Philosophy from St. Louis University, a Master of Divinity and Master of Theology from Columbia Theological Seminary, and a Bachelor of Arts from the University of Chattanooga.

Before his academic career, Dr. Arrington served in the U.S. Army from 1950–1953. He was a faculty member at Southeastern University in Lakeland, Fla. He has taught and lectured at many schools, local churches and conferences.

Dr. Arrington has been appointed to many boards and committees, such as the Literature Review Committee of Pathway Press, the Ordained Bishop's Examining Board for the state of Tennessee, the Church of God Commission for Doctrine and Polity, and the Committee to Evaluate Bible Curriculum for Christian Day Schools.

His books include *Divine Order in the Church*, *The Ministry of Reconciliation*, *The Acts of the Apostles*, the three-volume *Christian Doctrine: A Pentecostal Perspective*, *Exploring the Declaration of Faith*, *Encountering the Holy Spirit*, *The Spirit-Anointed Church*, *The Spirit-Anointed Jesus,* and *Unconditional Eternal Security: Myth or Truth?.*

Made in United States
Orlando, FL
30 December 2021

12673286R00178